First published in Great Britain 2022 by Farshore
An imprint of HarperCollins*Publishers*
1 London Bridge Street, London SE1 9GF
www.farshore.co.uk

HarperCollins*Publishers*
1st Floor, Watermarque Building, Ringsend Road
Dublin 4, Ireland

Written by Susie Rae

This book features illustrations by

Milivoj Ceran, Mark Molnar, Beth Trott, Julian Kok Joon Wen, Scott Murphy, Alex Stone, Aaron Hübrich, Slawomir Maniak, Dave Dorman, Conceptopolis, William O' Connor, Brynn Metheney, Carmen Sinek, E.M.Gist, Matt Stawicki, Robson Michel, Kekai Kotaki, Aaron Miller, Raphael-Lubke, Ryan Pancoast, Alessandra Pisano, Christopher Moeller, Aaron J.Riley, Chris, Seaman, Irina Nordsol, Cory Trego-Erdner, Jesper Ejsing, Robin Olausson, Andrew Mar, Robin Olausson, Jon Hodgson, Anna Pavleeva, Billy Christian, Eric Belisle, Mark Behm, Stacy Allan-William Doyle, Livia Prima, Mark Molnar , Robin Olausson, Dyson Logos, Grzegorz Rutkowski , Kieran Yanner, Claudio Pozas, Cynthia Sheppard, Rob Rey, Ralph Horsley, Andrew Mar, Sidharth Chaturvedi, Richard Whitters, Richard Whitters, Julian Joon Wen, Claudio Pozas, Michael Berube, Filip Burburan, Caroline Gariba, Caroline Gariba, Sam Keiser, Claudio Pozas, Sidharth Chaturvedi, Mark Behm, Zoltan Boros, Irina Nordsol, Chris Rallis, Piotr Dura, Manuel Castanon, Anna Podedworna, Adam Paquette, Piotr Dura, Titus Lunter, Alayna Lemmer, Ekaterina Burmak, Jared Blando, Cyril Van Der Haegen, Clint Cearley, Zuzanna Wuzyk, Raymond Swanland, Todd Lockwood, Adam Paquette, Mike Schley, Eric Belisle, Craig J Spearing, Anna Veltkamp

Additional images used under license from Shutterstock.com

ISBN 978 0 0085 1080 0
Printed in Romania
001

Stay safe online. Farshore is not responsible for content hosted by third parties..

MIX
Paper from
responsible sources
FSC™ C007454

This book is produced from independently certified FSC™ paper
to ensure responsible forest management.

For more information visit: www.harpercollins.co.uk/green

DUNGEONS & DRAGONS

ANNUAL 2023

CONTENTS

INTRODUCTION

From the early days of Advanced DUNGEONS & DRAGONS in the 1970s, all the way through to the convention-flooding, live-streaming, home-brewing fans today, D&D has been welcoming old and new fans alike for decades. Whether you're a veteran Dungeon Master or looking for your first ever game, the shores of the Forgotten Realms are here to welcome you!

Featuring all D&D's highlights over the past year, *DUNGEONS & DRAGONS Annual 2023* is packed full of world-shaping lore, hints, and tricks to level up your gaming table, exclusive interviews with creators, and fantastic puzzles to boost your Intelligence rolls. Discover campaign settings new and old, meet some of the most iconic characters from D&D lore, and brew up your own characters and mechanics, all within these pages.

SO WHAT ARE YOU WAITING FOR? GRAB YOUR DICE AND ROLL FOR INITIATIVE!

WELCOME TO THE MULTIVERSE

After nearly fifty years of worldbuilding, D&D has a whole multiverse on offer, ripe for exploration. From high-fantasy to steampunk and even an ancient-Greece-inspired plane, there really is a setting for everybody.

DEEPER INTO THE MULTIVERSE

With five editions of rules, not to mention countless novels, comics, video games, and board games, there are almost endless D&D settings stretching over forty years. You could explore the classic first edition worlds of Greyhawk and Blackmoor, traverse outer space in the Spelljammer setting, or even explore an ancient Greece-inspired universe with *Magic: the Gathering*'s Theros.

RAVENLOFT

Ideal for fans of a more gothic setting and horror games, the popular *Curse of Strahd* campaign is set in Ravenloft. Dark, spooky, beset with cursed mists and ruled over by a sinister and sadistic vampire, this is a world for only the bravest of adventurers.

THE FORGOTTEN REALMS

A true classic, the Forgotten Realms, and in particular the continent of Faerûn, have been the setting of more D&D games than you could possibly count. From the icy wastes of Icewind Dale to the tropical jungles of Chult, and the bustling cities of Waterdeep to the silence of the ethereal Neverwinter Wood, your party could explore the Realms for years and never see it all.

EBERRON

If you're a fan of steampunk aesthetics, pulp storylines, and sentient mechanical humanoids, then Eberron might be the setting for you. A world in the aftermath of a great war, Eberron offers a fun blend of technology and magic that provides endless opportunities for characters, stories, and mechanics.

EXANDRIA

Fans of the widely beloved actual play series *Critical Role* will be familiar with the world of Exandria, created by DM extraordinaire Matt Mercer. A high fantasy setting with original history and rich lore, it also has its own systems of magic, such as Dunamancy, and a whole host of fascinating cultures to get your teeth into.

STRIXHAVEN

A magical university on the plane of Arcavios, Strixhaven is perfect for a high-magic, high-fantasy roleplaying game. Originally from the world of *Magic: The Gathering*, Strixhaven is buzzing with opportunities for campaigns featuring clever NPCs, social shenanigans, and magical mayhem.

RAVNICA

Another setting from *Magic: The Gathering*, the plane of Ravnica is almost entirely taken up by a vast, sprawling city ruled over by twelve diverse guilds. For fans of urban settings, Ravnica offers an enormous amount of gameplay opportunities, including several of its own playable lineages – such as centaurs, minotaurs, and huge elephant-like Loxodons.

MORDENKAINEN PRESENTS: MONSTERS OF THE MULTIVERSE

Drawing on beasts and baddies from all over the multiverse, this official rulebook features dozens upon dozens of new stat blocks, as well as updated versions of more familiar creatures.

PLAYING ONLINE

After the Covid-19 pandemic trapped everyone in their homes, D&D games all over the world went online (because nothing can stop us playing). Even though in-person games are back now, online games still have lots to offer – especially as they let you play with people anywhere in the world.

GET THE TOOLKITS

There are plenty of online toolkits available, where you can combine and share all the resources you need for a game. Websites like Roll20 and Fantasy Grounds will let you create and maintain character sheets, stat blocks, magic items, battle maps, and any other info you need. They also let you share all your dice rolls ... so no more wondering if your rogue's third natural 20 in a row is genuine or not!

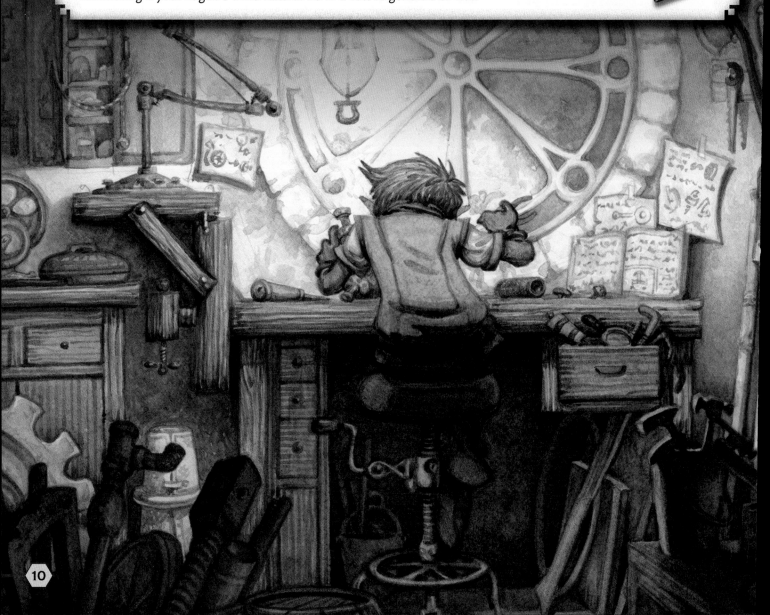

SHARE YOUR SCREEN

Screen sharing on video calling software opens up a whole new realm of possibilities for D&D games. DMs can share battle maps and dungeon puzzles, or you can go even further and start introducing web games to your sessions. Why not throw in a screen-shared game of *Tetris* or *Pacman* as part of a challenge? You can even share videos and music, to add to the drama of an encounter.

MESS AROUND ON ZOOM

What's the point of using video-calling software if you're not messing around with it? Change your names to something fitting the campaign and add atmospheric backgrounds. DMs can also take the opportunity to play around – suddenly introducing a guest player or turning off a player's camera and mic in a moment of drama can add extra tension to a key scene in your game.

GET YOUR HEAD IN THE GAME

When you're playing online, with the entire internet at your fingertips, it can be easy to get distracted – but try to stay focused. Switch off social media, put your phone away, and engross yourselves in the characters, story, and utter chaos of the game at hand!

PASS NOTES

An added bonus of playing online is being able to have private conversations without interrupting the flow of the game. Whether that's a player telling the DM about a secret action, the DM passing on some information to a lone player, or two PCs secretly plotting something together, private messaging adds a whole new level of entertainment to a game.

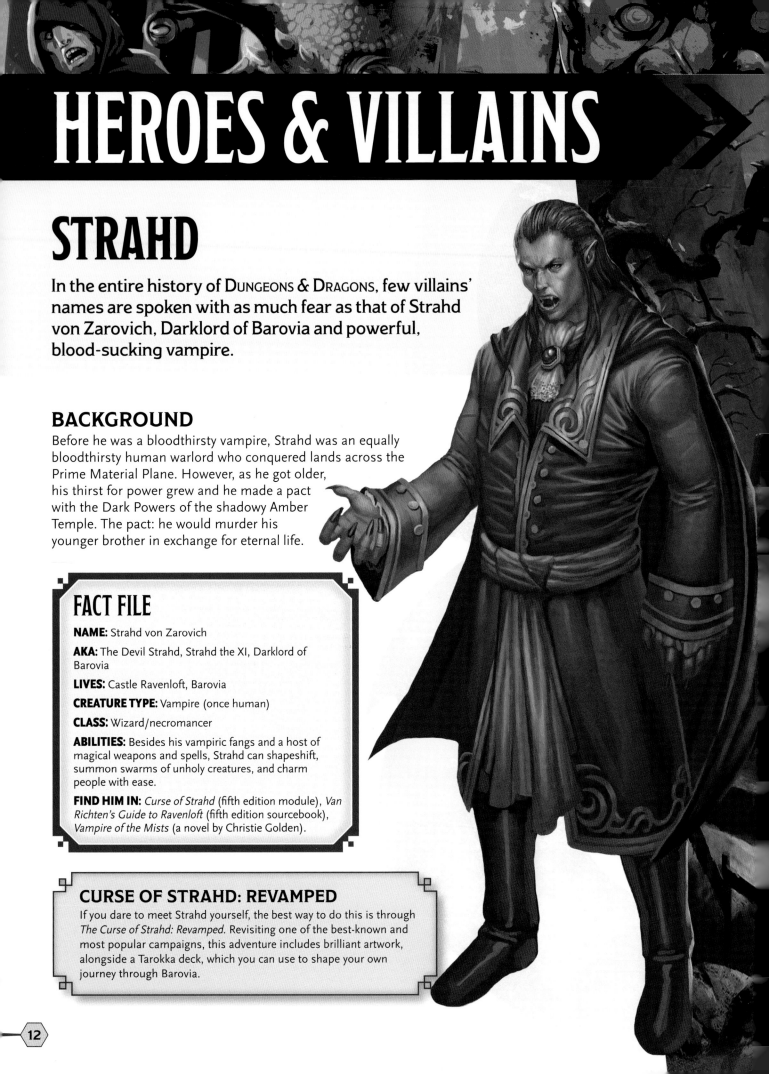

STRAHD

In the entire history of DUNGEONS & DRAGONS, few villains' names are spoken with as much fear as that of Strahd von Zarovich, Darklord of Barovia and powerful, blood-sucking vampire.

BACKGROUND

Before he was a bloodthirsty vampire, Strahd was an equally bloodthirsty human warlord who conquered lands across the Prime Material Plane. However, as he got older, his thirst for power grew and he made a pact with the Dark Powers of the shadowy Amber Temple. The pact: he would murder his younger brother in exchange for eternal life.

FACT FILE

NAME: Strahd von Zarovich

AKA: The Devil Strahd, Strahd the XI, Darklord of Barovia

LIVES: Castle Ravenloft, Barovia

CREATURE TYPE: Vampire (once human)

CLASS: Wizard/necromancer

ABILITIES: Besides his vampiric fangs and a host of magical weapons and spells, Strahd can shapeshift, summon swarms of unholy creatures, and charm people with ease.

FIND HIM IN: *Curse of Strahd* (fifth edition module), *Van Richten's Guide to Ravenloft* (fifth edition sourcebook), *Vampire of the Mists* (a novel by Christie Golden).

CURSE OF STRAHD: REVAMPED

If you dare to meet Strahd yourself, the best way to do this is through *The Curse of Strahd: Revamped*. Revisiting one of the best-known and most popular campaigns, this adventure includes brilliant artwork, alongside a Tarokka deck, which you can use to shape your own journey through Barovia.

WELCOME TO RAVENLOFT

Strahd's home – and prison – is a gothic castle in the valley of Barovia, a land that was once part of the Prime Material Plane, but was transported to the Shadowfell after Strahd sold his soul to the Dark Powers. Once a thriving valley, it is now cold and forbidding, surrounded by freezing magical mists, with very little sunlight, even during the day. The locals live in constant fear of their dark master, who rules with an iron fist.

VAMPIRES

These powerful undead creatures are legendary D&D monsters. Notoriously difficult to kill, they lurk in the darkness and prey on the unwary with their insatiable thirst for blood.

WHO WAS TATYANA?

While still a human, Strahd fell in love with the beautiful Tatyana, fiancée of his brother, Sergei. After killing Sergei at the behest of the Dark Powers, Strahd pursued Tatyana across his castle grounds, but she threw herself from the top of his castle rather than marry him. In his grief, Strahd attempted to take his own life too, but instead he found himself imprisoned in the Shadowfell, unable to leave or die.

ALLIES & ENEMIES

DOCTOR RUDOLPH VAN RICHTEN

Perhaps the greatest monster hunter of all time, Dr. Rudolph van Richten is cursed to outlive all his friends and allies ... but this gives him plenty of time to attempt to hunt down and kill the Devil Strahd.

THE DARK POWERS

Residing in the Amber Temple, these entities are a haven of powerful dark magic. They influenced Strahd into killing his own brother and are the reason that Barovia is both his domain to rule over and a prison.

JANDER SUNSTAR

Strahd is not the only powerful vampire in the realms. He has a long-standing rivalry with sun elf vampire Jander Sunstar, whose love for a young woman that Strahd shares a history with leads him to hate the Darklord of Barovia.

THE VISTANI

While not friends of Strahd, this travelling civilisation of fortune tellers has a tentative alliance with Strahd. They are one of the few peoples who can navigate his impassable mists and enter and leave Barovia at will.

COMBAT CHAOS

The party is trying to put together the events after a particularly chaotic battle. These six pictures show each party member's version of their exploit – which two are identical?

DWARF

FIGHTER

PALADIN

WIZARD

BARBARIAN

ELF

WHAT HAVE YOU HOARD?

After defeating a powerful green dragon, it's time to claim some well-earned loot! Can you find the following items among the dragon's hoard?

Helm of Brilliance, 2 x golden goblets, 6 x rubies, 4 x sapphires, 4 x emeralds, The Ring of Winter, The Staff of the Magi, Book of legendary spells

ANSWERS ON PAGES 92-93

RAVENLOFT

For those who enjoy the darker side of D&D, the demiplane of Ravenloft is the ideal campaign setting. The home of legendary vampire overlord Strahd, it's filled with vicious beasts, dark sorcerers and shadowy intrigue.

THE DARK POWERS

Very little is known of the Dark Powers who rule over Ravenloft – they are a shadowy, malevolent force of a largely unknown nature. Though most people manage to avoid the notice of the Dark Powers, those who show a particular affinity for evil may attract their attention, or even manage to make a deal with them.

DARK GIFTS

If you make a deal with the Dark Powers, they may bestow a gift upon you – new abilities, spells, or skills. However, think before you make that pact, as every gift comes with a cost that may overwhelm you.

VAN RICHTEN'S GUIDE TO RAVENLOFT

This official fifth edition sourcebook gives a greater insight into the spooky world of Ravenloft than ever before. It collects new player lineages, subclasses for bards and warlocks, and a new mechanic for pacts made with the Dark Powers, along with fascinating new lore.

WHO IS VAN RICHTEN?

Cursed by a vengeful Vistani to have everyone he loves killed by a monster, Dr. Rudolph van Richten dedicated his life to hunting those monsters. Now, he lives in Ravenloft, determined to study and eventually kill Strahd.

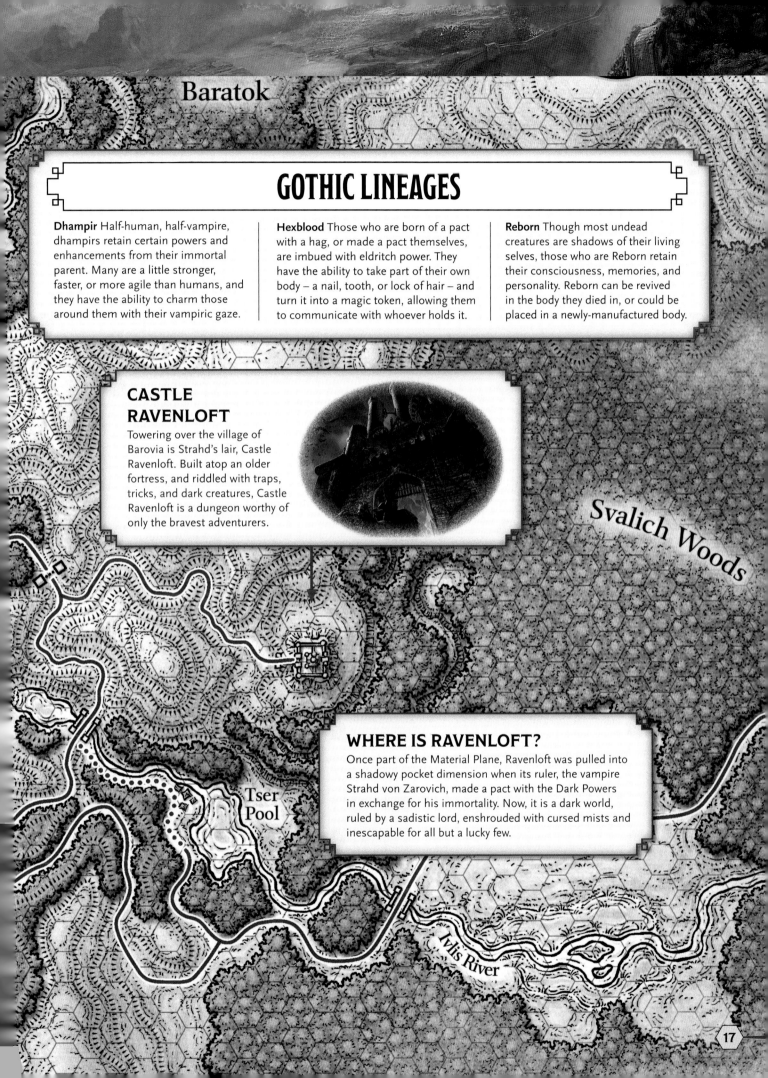

GOTHIC LINEAGES

Dhampir Half-human, half-vampire, dhampirs retain certain powers and enhancements from their immortal parent. Many are a little stronger, faster, or more agile than humans, and they have the ability to charm those around them with their vampiric gaze.

Hexblood Those who are born of a pact with a hag, or made a pact themselves, are imbued with eldritch power. They have the ability to take part of their own body – a nail, tooth, or lock of hair – and turn it into a magic token, allowing them to communicate with whoever holds it.

Reborn Though most undead creatures are shadows of their living selves, those who are Reborn retain their consciousness, memories, and personality. Reborn can be revived in the body they died in, or could be placed in a newly-manufactured body.

CASTLE RAVENLOFT

Towering over the village of Barovia is Strahd's lair, Castle Ravenloft. Built atop an older fortress, and riddled with traps, tricks, and dark creatures, Castle Ravenloft is a dungeon worthy of only the bravest adventurers.

Svalich Woods

WHERE IS RAVENLOFT?

Once part of the Material Plane, Ravenloft was pulled into a shadowy pocket dimension when its ruler, the vampire Strahd von Zarovich, made a pact with the Dark Powers in exchange for his immortality. Now, it is a dark world, ruled by a sadistic lord, enshrouded with cursed mists and inescapable for all but a lucky few.

Tser Pool

Ivlis River

ROLL FOR GENEROSITY

It's not just the incredible imagination and commitment to amazing gameplay that makes your D&D community so great – it's your unbeatable generosity. Every year, players, DMs, game designers, podcasters, and streamers from the D&D community rally together to raise money for charity. Why not get involved?

EXTRA LIFE

Extra Life is a massive annual fundraising drive in the gaming community, pushing donations for the Children's Hospitals Network.

Charity Streams

There are countless D&D livestreams on Twitch.tv for Extra Life every year, with DMs and players putting on a show to encourage viewers to dig deep and donate.

Charity Adventures

Besides streams, Wizards of the Coast release exclusive adventures through the Adventurers League, with all proceeds going to Extra Life. Why not grab a copy of *Minsc & Boo's Journal of Villainy*, featuring the iconic ranger and hamster duo's thoughts on settings, locations, monsters, and villains? Or for those who like the weirder side of things, there's *Domains of Delight*, an official companion to *The Wild Beyond the Witchlight*.

Merchandise

Every year, D&D also produces exciting Extra Life merchandise inspired by their most recent adventures. Past year's event shirts have featured *Rime of the Frostmaiden's* three kobolds in a trench coat, and *Wild Beyond the Witchlight's* adorable displacer beast.

How Do I Get Involved?

We're very glad you asked! There are loads of ways to get involved. You can tune into D&D's official Twitch channel to catch a livestream and donate, or you can even run your own charity stream through the Extra Life website.

PLAYING D&D FOR COMIC RELIEF

Every year, DMs and players get together to raise money for UK charity Comic Relief. In past years, this has ranged from celebrity livestream Comic Relief Plays DUNGEONS & DRAGONS to the opportunity to attend epic, real-life events. In 2022, D&D fans bid for the opportunity to go on an incredible island adventure, featuring in-person games run by Oxventure DM Johnny Chiodini.

PLAYING D&D FOR MERMAIDS

As part of Digipride, an online gaming event that supports the LGBTQ+ community, D&D recently put on an official charity livestream to raise money for Mermaids, a charity that supports trans and non-binary youth. DMed by the incomparable Luyanda Unati Lewis-Nyawo of Three Black Halflings, the hugely successful stream featured doctoral researchers and creators Shaaba and Jammi Dodger, YouTuber Rowan Ellis, writer Jason Okundaye, and drag performer Charity Kase.

PLANNING A DUNGEON DELVE

While exploring a sprawling world or meeting a host of NPCs is always fun, there's nothing more classic D&D than a dungeon delve: a series of encounters in a contained location, leading towards loot, a boss fight, or the next exciting step on the quest.

CREATING A SETTING

The first step to creating a dungeon is deciding where to put it. Where might a dungeon sit in the setting of your campaign? It could be in an actual dungeon – beneath a castle, or in the local prison – in a haunted house, hidden cave, or villain's lair.

COMBAT

A dungeon isn't a dungeon without a combat encounter or two! The *Monster Manual* is full of beasts that you can throw at your players, from giant rats and goblins that will train-up low-level parties, to dragons and demons who can challenge veteran players. Look at the challenge rating if you're unsure how easy or difficult the encounter should be.

ROLEPLAY ENCOUNTERS

If you have a party that enjoys roleplay, there's no reason why you can't include some RP in a dungeon. They may stumble upon another adventuring party, a villain that can be tricked or persuaded rather than fought, or simply a creature who lives in the dungeon that they can chat with.

BE PREPARED

As dungeons usually don't have much opportunity for long rests, make sure the party is prepared with hit points, spell slots, potions, and weapons before they get started.

PUZZLES AND RIDDLES

Not everything in a dungeon has to be combat! Try adding puzzles and riddles to test your players' intelligence. Be creative – you could throw in a game of minesweeper or chess, or a creative word puzzle they need to solve to advance to the next stage of the dungeon.

A	B	C	D	E	F	G	H	I	J	K	L	M
o	*o*	*ə*	*ɗ*	*v*	*v*	*ɓ*	*y*	*ɔ*	*ɗ*	*ɓ*	*v*	

N	O	P	Q	R	S	T	U	V	W	X	Y	Z
ɑ	*ɔ*	*f*	*L*	*ʃ*	*b*	*ʋ*	*ρ*	*ω*	*κ*	*ʮ*	*ʒ*	*ʊ*

FIND INSPIRATION

If you're struggling for ideas, consider building your dungeon around a theme. A necromancer's lair could contain undead monsters, or a dragon's hoard may be protected by puzzles based on their specific element, such as a fiery entrance to a red dragon's cave.

TRAPS

In between encounters, you can lay all sorts of traps for the party to stumble into or, if they roll high enough, find and avoid. This keeps the players on their toes, and it adds a sense of danger to the dungeon.

ENDGAME

Every dungeon should end with a satisfying endgame. This is usually a high-powered fight, but could also be a particularly tricky puzzle, a trek across a dangerous crevasse, or a death-defying journey through a hallway of dangerous traps.

D&D BOOKSHELF

If you love the vast fantasy worlds of D&D, then why not pick up one of the hundreds of novels set in the Forgotten Realms and beyond? Containing the adventures of some of fantasy's most iconic heroes, here's your handy guide on where to start.

MEET AN ICONIC HERO

There are few heroes in the Forgotten Realms better known than drow ranger Drizzt Do'Urden. Created by D&D icon R.A. Salvatore, the adventures of Drizzt and his party, the Companions of the Hall, have shaped the Realms, from Icewind Dale to Menzoberranzan.

Where to Start?

There are dozens of books featuring Drizzt, but the best place to start is at the very beginning. Drizzt first appeared in *The Icewind Dale Trilogy*.

DIVE INTO AN EPIC SAGA

There are over 150 books in the *Dragonlance* series – so this is definitely one for the hardcore readers! Taking place on the world of Krynn, the adventures within are set against a backdrop of a constant war between the gods of good and evil.

Where to Start?

With so many books, why not get started with a self-contained mini-series? *The Dragonlance Legends Trilogy* has it all: loveable characters, time travel, and sinister villains.

DISCOVER A DARKER TALE

Set in the dark domain of Ravenloft, a sinister world ruled over by the legendary vampire and warlord Strahd von Zarovich, the 22-part *Ravenloft* series has a horror-tinged edge to it. If you love everything dark, gothic, and spooky, these are the books for you!

Where to Start?

Vampire of the Mists is the first book in the series – and one of the best. Starring Jander Sunstar, elf vampire and brooding hero extraordinaire, it's also one of the most-loved books featuring Strahd.

TRY A TASTE OF EVERYTHING

The Sundering books are a fantastic read for somebody who wants to sample all different parts of D&D's rich lore. Each book is a standalone adventure, written by a different D&D author.

Where to Start?

The first Sundering title, *The Companions*, by R.A. Salvatore, follows iconic hero Drizzt and his friends, The Companions. If you're new to D&D books, this is the perfect point of entry.

FIND SOMETHING NEW

The glut of available D&D books from over forty years can be daunting – so *Dragonlance: Dragons of Deceit* is ideal if you want to pick up something on the newer side. It's the first in the rebooted Dragonlance book series, based on the popular setting from the 1980s, with a new protagonist and a few older faces.

GO BEYOND HIGH FANTASY

If you're looking for a slightly different setting, the *Dreaming Dark Trilogy* is set in the low-magic, steampunk world of Eberron. These books contain plane-hopping shenanigans, gripping mysteries and heroes living in the aftermath of a massive war.

SOMETHING FOR YOUNGER READERS

D&D is beloved by players of all ages, and *Dungeon Academy: No Humans Allowed* is a brilliant story aimed at younger fans. Follow the adventures of Zelli Stormclash, a human who disguises herself as a minotaur to attend the monsters-only Dungeon Academy, alongside a group of loveable misfits.

CANDLEKEEP MYSTERIES

Players who love a one-shot and DMs who are looking for a side-quest to add to their long-running campaign are going to love *Candlekeep Mysteries*, an anthology of mini-campaigns written by some of the best, brightest, and funniest names in the D&D community.

WELCOME TO CANDLEKEEP

Candlekeep is a library fortress full to the brim with magical tomes of every type. Whether they're looking for an ancient scroll of lore or a bizarre, cursed book, scholars, mages, and historians from all around the multiverse are drawn to the library in pursuit of rare arcane knowledge.

THE JOY OF EXTRADIMENSIONAL SPACES

When your party discovered the lost entry to a mage's extradimensional mansion, you were trapped inside and must find a way to escape. Part mystery, part dungeon delve, with lots of fun NPCs, puzzles, and mini-combats to get your teeth into, this is a brilliant tale for newer players who want a taste of the game.

SHEMSHIME'S BEDTIME RHYME

Within the stacks of Candlekeep itself lie many strange books. One such tome, a book of bizarre nursery rhymes, will see your party cursed and quarantined in a spooky cellar. Any horror fans will love this straightforward but extremely creepy game.

THE PRICE OF BEAUTY

What's better than a spa episode? In this adventure, your party get to travel to a restful spa where they can relax ... and maybe discover what happened to that missing acolyte. A great session for players who are looking for a more roleplay-heavy session, featuring plenty of interesting NPCs to interact with.

KANDLEKEEP DEKONSTRUKTION

By far one of the silliest campaigns in the collection, Kandlekeep Dekonstruktion sees your party attempting to stop the Livestock, a group of Candlekeep custodians-turned-cultists who have decided to fire part of the library into space. Perfect for more experienced players who revel in a bit of chaos.

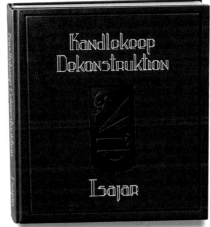

THE CANOPIC BEING

A brilliant, classic delve through a trap-filled dungeon, The Canopic Being features a book containing names of "willing sacrifices" for an evil mummy lord ... including the party themselves. Now, you're tasked with finding out why, to ensure you don't end up being consumed.

XANTHORIA

Only for experienced players who like a bit of high-level action, Xanthoria features a mysterious and deadly plague that's sweeping the Sword Coast, a lichen lich (get it?) and some very hefty combats with some creepy, fungal monsters.

BESTIARY

FIENDS AND CELESTIALS

In the depths of the Lower Planes and the heights of the Upper Planes live some of the strangest, fiercest, and most powerful creatures in - or above, or below - the Forgotten Realms. Often, devils, demons, and celestials will venture to the Material Plane to interact or entertain themselves with mortals.

IMP

CHALLENGE RATING: 1

Though not the most powerful fiends, these tiny, shapeshifting devils can deliver a nasty sting using their venomous tails. They often work for more powerful beings, and sometimes serve as wizards' familiars.

WHAT CAN THEY DO?

Beyond their vicious stinging tails, imps can polymorph into other.

small animals (such as rats, ravens and spiders) or turn invisible.

WHERE DO YOU FIND THEM?

The Nine Hells, though they often come to the Material Plane, either because they have been summoned, or because they're seeking mischief.

BATTLE PLAN

They're resistant to most regular attacks, including spells, and cannot be damaged with fire, so your best bet is to prepare for battle with magical weapons.

BALOR

CHALLENGE RATING: 19

These high-ranking demons are creatures of absolute fire, exuding white-hot flame from their very being. They thrive in chaos and violence, and are often generals of the demonic armies when the devils and demons go to war.

WHAT CAN THEY DO?

They are ferocious in battle, fighting with a longsword and whip, and doing massive amounts of damage.

with the fiery aura that surrounds them. Be extra careful, because even if you do kill them, they will explode!

WHERE DO YOU FIND THEM?

The Abyss.

BATTLE PLAN

Don't even think about going up against a balor until you're a high-enough level to survive. When you do, prep magic weapons and anything that may be fire-resistant.

PEGASUS

CHALLENGE RATING: 2

Pegasi are good-natured, winged horses. Though they are generally quite shy around other species, when a person is pure-hearted enough to tame one, they will be fiercely loyal for life.

WHAT CAN THEY DO?

Pegasi have an innate ability to tell where the person riding them sits on the spectrum between good and evil.

WHERE DO YOU FIND THEM?

Forests of the Prime Material Plane, or the Outer Plane of Arborea.

BATTLE PLAN

If you do find yourself up against a pegasus, be wary of their hooves, which can deliver a hefty kick. They're also very wise, so difficult to trick or sneak past.

SOLAR

CHALLENGE RATING: 21

These are the most powerful angels in the Upper Planes, directly serving the good-aligned deities. They often come accompanied by other angels, or other beings of good, particularly phoenixes and titans.

WHAT CAN THEY DO?

What can't they do? Besides their powerful holy weapons, they can teleport, fly and emit searing, celestial energy. They can also blind enemies with their gaze, and have powerful healing magic.

WHERE DO YOU FIND THEM?

The Upper Planes.

BATTLE PLAN

Prepare yourself with magical weapons, and make sure your mage has a restoration spell stocked. Solars can't be charmed, exhausted, frightened or poisoned, so plan your magical attacks accordingly.

DEVIL OR DEMON?

Is there a difference between devils and demons? Absolutely! Though both hail from the Lower Planes, devils are generally creatures of law, while demons thrive in chaos. War between the two is not uncommon.

A BEGINNER'S GUIDE TO HOMEBREWING

Many DMs and players enjoy creating worlds and characters that don't exist anywhere in the official D&D sourcebooks. Homebrewing your own material can be a lot of fun, so this handy guide is here to show you where to start.

CREATING A CHARACTER

Classes

Homebrewing classes is a little trickier, but that's no reason not to take a crack at it! A good place to start is to take a look at existing classes and decide which features you want to include. Will your character be a spellcaster? If so, how many spells and spell slots will they have? Which spell lists will they be able to access? If they're a martial character, consider what their combat capabilities will be. Finding a balance is key – having a character that's too powerful is no fun, but neither is having one that's too weak.

Lineages

A good place to start when homebrewing a character is deciding on their lineage. The simplest way to do this is to use the official variant human option – increase two ability scores by one, or one by two, add proficiency to one skill, then select a feat for your character.

Feats

There are dozens of feats available, which you can easily build into your character to customise them.

The *Player's Handbook* contains a lot of good ones, or you can create your own based on your character's backstory.

I lie about almost everything, even when there's no good reason to

PERSONALITY TRAITS

Creativity. I never run the same con twice.

IDEALS

I owe everything to my mentor – a horrible person who's probably rotting in jail somewhere.

BONDS

I can't resist swindling people who are more powerful than me.

FLAWS

BUILDING A WORLD

Geography

When creating the geography of a world from scratch, start small. It's all very well to create massive, sprawling maps, but this can be daunting and exhausting, especially if your players take five sessions to leave the tavern! Start with a single town or city, and then a few surrounding areas that your characters might want to explore. Once the campaign's moving, you can flesh the world out as you go.

Magic Systems

Is magic commonplace in your world? How do people feel about it? Having an area with low magic or a general mistrust of magic can offer some cool story beats for caster characters.

Politics

The politics of a world can provide endless opportunities for gameplay. Is your world at war or in a time of peace? If there are wars happening, what factions are involved? If you're basing your game in a city, are there guilds or gangs around? Who rules the area? From here, your party can decide how law-abiding they are, and whose quests they want to take on.

MAKING MAGIC ITEMS

Sooner or later, most DMs will start playing around with magic items. When you're making your own, consider how powerful you want it to be. Will it enhance existing skills or cause damage on its own? Will it mimic the effects of a particular spell? How many times can it be used? Are there any negative consequences from using it?

TOMB RAIDERS

After working their way through a trap-riddled dungeon, the party have loaded up with loot and are ready to go ... but the traps have reset themselves. Using the instructions written by the rogue, lead the party through the dungeon to safety. Which square holds the exit?

N7, E9, S2, E2, S1, W4, N5, W3, S1, W4, N6, E5, S3, E7, N2, E2, S1

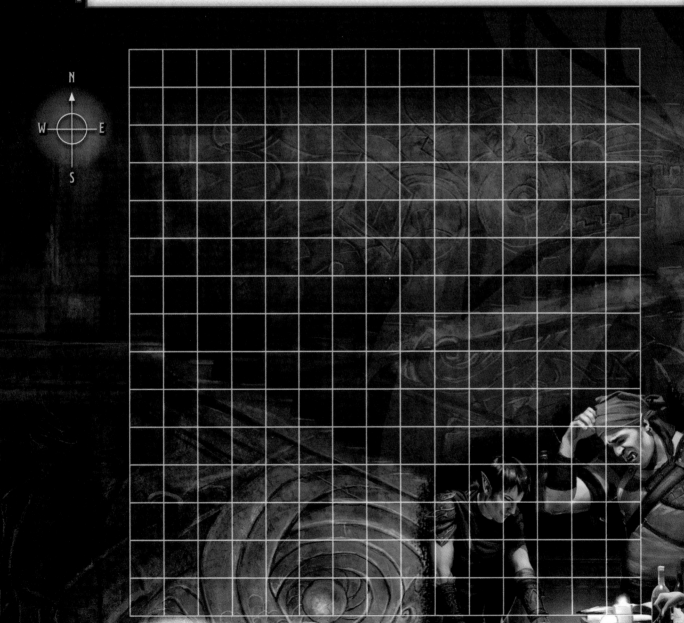

↑ START

IT'S NOT WHAT YOU SPHINX

While exploring another dungeon, the party come up against a powerful sphinx. Which of these shadows belongs to the sphinx?

ACERERAK

If you're talking about liches, one name springs to mind before any other: Acererak. This beyond-powerful lich delights in collecting almighty relics and hiding them away in deadly, trap-filled dungeons, just so he can watch adventurers struggle and die.

BACKGROUND

Most knowledge of Acererak's early life before he became a lich has been lost to the ages, but we know this: he gained much of his power by harvesting the souls of those who died in his tombs and dungeons, trapping them in his phylactery. Eventually, he travelled to the city of Omu, defeated the Nine Trickster Gods who ruled there and buried them in yet another lethal dungeon.

LICHES

Corrupted wizards who sacrifice their soul in exchange for immortality and untold power, liches are notoriously hard to kill. They seal their souls in phylacteries, and cannot be fully destroyed unless their phylactery is also destroyed.

FACT FILE

NAME: Acererak the Eternal

AKA: The Devourer, Lord of Unlife, Acererak of the Scarlet Robes

LIVES: Any of his trap-riddled lairs

CREATURE TYPE: Fiendish demilich

CLASS: Wizard

ABILITIES: He has incredible spellcasting abilities, casting spells up to level nine (included the dreaded *power word kill*). He can also drain the life force from his enemies with his *disrupt life* ability.

FIND HIM IN: *Tomb of Annihilation*, *Tales from the Yawning Portal* (Tomb of Horrors)

TOMB OF ANNIHILATION

As Acererak's Soulmonger unleashes a Death Curse on the Forgotten Realms, this L1-L10 campaign sees a party travel to Chult to find and destroy the dark device ... before it destroys half of Faerûn.

THE TOMB OF HORRORS

This classic first edition campaign saw Acererak introduced for the first time, in a notoriously deadly dungeon. Very few parties make it through in one piece, and if they do, then they are then faced with Acererak himself at the very end.

THE SOULMONGER

After building the Tomb of Nine Gods, Acererak enlisted a coven of hags to create this powerful artefact. It drained and trapped the souls of anyone in the Forgotten Realms who had died and been revived in the past, allowing Acererak to gain massively in power.

THE TOMB OF NINE GODS

One of Acererak's most twisted creations is the Tomb of Annihilation on the continent of Chult. The city of Omu was once dedicated to Nine Trickster Gods. However, on Acererak's arrival, he killed those gods, forced the people of Omu to build a great tomb for them, and then killed the people, burying their bodies with those of their gods. This became the Tomb of Annihilation, perhaps Acererak's most lethal lair.

THE NINE TRICKSTER GODS

Ijin, an almiraj goddess, **Kubazan**, a froghemoth god, **Moa**, a jaculi goddess, **Nangnang**, a grung goddess, **Orbo'laka**, a zorbo goddess, **Papazotl**, an eblis god, **Shagambi**, a kamadan goddess, **Unkh**, a flail snail goddess, **Wongo**, a su-monster god.

THE FEYWILD

A step to the left of the Material Plane, you might find the Feywild, a staggeringly beautiful world filled with unpredictable, primal magic. Be cautious – the Feywild is a dangerous, chaotic place that shows very little mercy to those who stumble onto the wrong side of those who live there.

WHERE IS THE FEYWILD?

Like Ravenloft, the Feywild is a parallel plane to the Material Plane, with very similar features – though the geography of the Feywild seems to be constantly moving and changing. The route to the Feywild is also regularly shifting – if you look hard enough, you may happen upon a fey crossing in an ancient forest or crumbling ruin, or you may simply stumble into the plane by pure accident.

Sirocco Straits

PEOPLE OF THE FEYWILD

FAIRIES

Native to the Feywild, these tiny humanoids are infused with the magic of their home plane, making them natural spellcasters. Their insect-like wings allow them to fly as easily as walk, meaning that these little beings can dart through the forests of the Feywild with ease.

ELADRIN

Eladrin are a type of elf who call the Feywild their home, eladrin have a primal kind of magic that is inherently linked to nature. Their appearance and abilities change according to their ever-shifting moods, which relate to the four seasons.

HARENGON

Curious, rabbit-like creatures, harengons love nothing more than to travel across the worlds, discovering all they can along the way. Even when they aren't in the Feywild, they carry the luck of their home with them, enabling them to leap out of trouble easily.

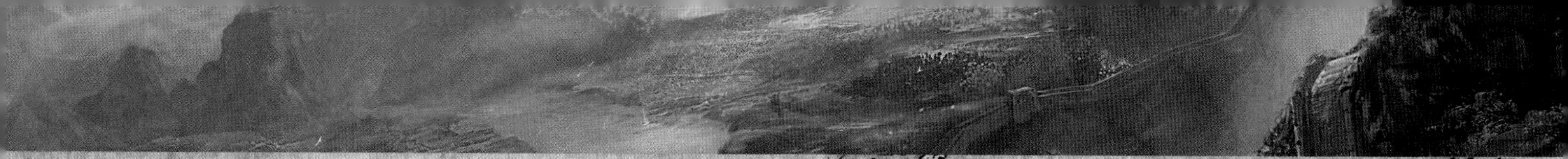

THE WILD BEYOND THE WITCHLIGHT

Explore the Feywild in greater depth than ever before in official campaign *The Wild Beyond the Witchlight*. Including new races, NPCs, monsters, character backgrounds, and settings, this campaign combines whimsical, fun encounters with some downright scary foes and brilliant magic mechanics.

Swamp of Oblivion
(Plane of Ooze)

Sea of Worlds

Mud Hills

PRISMEER

Prismeer, in the heart of the Feywild, was once a single domain under the protection of archfey Zybilna. As of *The Wild Beyond the Witchlight*, however, Prismeer has been fractured into three parts: the swamp of Hither, the ancient forest of Thither, and the mountainscape of Yon.

Feywild

Material Plane

City of Jewels

The Furnaces

Fountains of Creation
(Plane of Magma)

THE SEELIE AND UNSEELIE COURTS

Traditionally, the Feywild is controlled by two opposing courts. The bright and playful Seelie, or Summer, Court is ruled by Queen Titania, while the dark, sinister Unseelie Court is under the rule of the mysterious Queen of Air and Darkness.

Fountains of Creation

Plane of Fire

THREE BLACK HALFLINGS

If you don't know who the *Three Black Halflings* are, get ready to meet your new favourite podcast. Jeremy Cobb, Jasper William Cartwright, and all-new halfling Olivia Kennedy are joined by a host of RPG talent to discuss everything Dungeons & Dragons.

GETTING INVESTED

There's very little the halflings love more than the flexibility and creativity that the world of D&D has to offer, for both DMs and players. Jasper William Cartwright talks about how the freedom to homebrew can work for players: "I think if you give people the option of having control in the world and getting to homebrew stuff around the characters, then naturally people are a little bit more invested in the game."

© *Three Black Halflings*

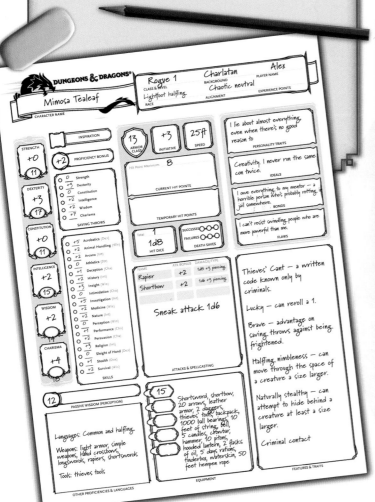

CHANGING THE RECIPE

While new players may be intimidated by the depth of D&D's lore, the halflings are here to reassure you. "It's a bit like cooking," Jasper says of his worldbuilding style. "When you start off cooking, there's this assumption that it's super complicated and you have to throw in all of the ingredients at once. Generally, I was surprised by how little I needed — in terms of lore — to successfully run a lot of my sessions."

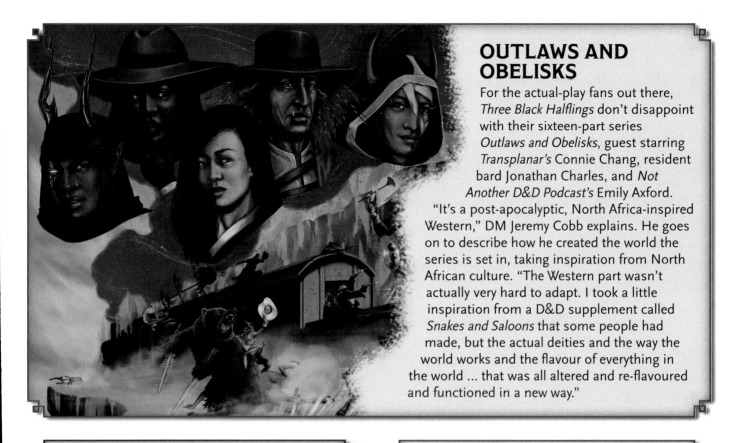

OUTLAWS AND OBELISKS

For the actual-play fans out there, *Three Black Halflings* don't disappoint with their sixteen-part series *Outlaws and Obelisks*, guest starring *Transplanar's* Connie Chang, resident bard Jonathan Charles, and *Not Another D&D Podcast's* Emily Axford.

"It's a post-apocalyptic, North Africa-inspired Western," DM Jeremy Cobb explains. He goes on to describe how he created the world the series is set in, taking inspiration from North African culture. "The Western part wasn't actually very hard to adapt. I took a little inspiration from a D&D supplement called *Snakes and Saloons* that some people had made, but the actual deities and the way the world works and the flavour of everything in the world ... that was all altered and re-flavoured and functioned in a new way."

EMBRACING THE COMMUNITY

With dozens of brilliant guest stars getting involved, including *Dimension 20's* Brennan Lee Mulligan and Zac Oyama, DM extraordinaire B. Dave Walters, and *Transplanar's* Connie Chang, the halflings are incredibly proud of their community. "One of the things that has been outstanding is that the community has rallied around us," Jasper says. "It's a very humbling experience. I've gotten quite emotional about the success of this show."

CHANGING HALFLINGS

After original halfling Luyanda Unati Lewis-Nyawo moved on to pursue their acting career, Jeremy and Jasper were excited to welcome Olivia Kennedy to the podcast.

GEM DRAGONS

Undeniably, Dragons are the most iconic creatures in D&D, and the lore surrounding them is rich and exciting. Until recently, we were only aware of two broad groups of dragons – chromatic and metallic – but now, with *Fizban's Treasury of Dragons*, we're introduced to a brand new, extra shiny type of dragon: the gem dragon.

FIZBAN'S TREASURY OF DRAGONS

Discover more about dragons than ever before in this brilliant tome, brought to you by archmage Fizban the Fabulous. Featuring options for dragon characters, suggestions for dragon-based games and a whole host of new dragons, this book is a must-have for all dragon lovers.

CRYSTAL DRAGONS

High in the iciest, most beautiful mountain peaks, you may be lucky enough to come across the lair of a crystal dragon. The most sociable of dragons, crystal dragons are the most likely to entertain explorers or adventurers who happen upon their homes, and may even allow visitors to marvel at their hoard.

AMETHYST DRAGONS

You're most likely to find these solitary creatures in watery lairs, perhaps behind a waterfall or near a quiet lake. Amethyst dragons are great lovers of knowledge, and their hoards are often filled with scholarly tomes and scrolls, and interesting scientific instruments.

TOPAZ DRAGONS

There's no place that a topaz dragon is happier than by the sea, and they're obsessed with anything related to the ocean and seafaring. They can be quite vain beasts, and adore mirrors, which they cover their lairs with so that they can admire their own reflections.

EMERALD DRAGONS

Emerald dragons are, by nature, often very paranoid creatures who will construct labyrinthine lairs to repel visitors and, Bahamut forbid, looters. Perhaps more than most dragons, they adore gold, and can often tell you exactly how much gold is in their lair, down to the last coin.

MOONSTONE DRAGONS

These curious and fanciful dragons like to straddle the boundary between the Material Plane and the Feywild, and often spread their lairs over numerous locations across planes. If you wish to please a moonstone dragon, then offering up the most unique or bizarre item you can find for their hoard is a good start.

SAPPHIRE DRAGONS

Perhaps the most warlike of the gem dragons, sapphire dragons very rarely get involved in the affairs of humanoids – unless there's something in it for them. Their hoards are often peppered with the spoils of various wars, which they organise meticulously, to their own very specific system.

WRITING A

A CHARACTER CREATION CHECKLIST

Creating your character is one of the most exciting parts of any new D&D game, and what's a player character without a really juicy backstory? You may have your character's whole life cooked up in your head already, but if not, this checklist will get you started.

CHILDHOOD

A character's childhood can have a huge impact on how they act as an adult, factors such as where they were born, if they were an only child or their education are key things to think about.

- Who were their parents?
- Were they rich or poor?
- Where did they grow up?
- Were they part of a community?
- What did the community think about them?
- Why did they leave home?

A good, straightforward way to start a character build is with three simple questions: What does your character want? What do they need? And what do they fear? This is a great foundation to build on, and will help you shape their motivations and personality.

RELATIONSHIPS

How you talk to new people could be linked to your past relationships, and not just the romantic ones. Sit back, relax and tell me about your character's mother.

- Does your character have a close parent or mentor?
- Have they been a member of any guilds, factions or other groups?
- How do those groups feel about them now?
- Do they have any enemies or rivals?
- Do they have many friends?
- Do they like strangers?

BACKSTORY

PREVIOUS EMPLOYMENT

There's a reason people always ask, "So, what do you do?" Giving your character a career is a great way to learn more about them.

- What does your character do for a living?
- Are they good at it?
- Have they had other jobs?
- Who do they work with?
- What do they think of these people?
- What do they enjoy?

VALUES

Some more abstract questions to consider for your character are based on what they believe in.

- What is your character's key motivation?
- What do they love?
- What do they hate?
- What are they afraid of?
- What is their outlook on life?
- Are they selfish or selfless?

SPELLING IT OUT

While questing, the party have come across a door that can only be opened using a specific spell. Grab your *Player's Handbook* and use the clues written below to work out which spell the party's wizard needs.

THE SPELL IS LEVEL 2 OR HIGHER
IT CANNOT BE CAST BY A STANDARD BARD
IT IS AN EVOCATION SPELL
IT CANNOT REACH FURTHER THAN 100 FT

CHARM PERSON
EARTH TREMOR
MAGIC MISSILE
PYROTECHNICS
ROPE TRICK
SHATTER
SPIDER CLIMB
SLEET STORM
MAJOR IMAGE
FIREBALL
LIGHTNING BOLT
ELEMENTAL BANE
CONTROL WATER
POLYMORPH

ANSWERS ON PAGES 92-93

CASHING IN

The party have just been paid handsomely for a recent quest, but there's one problem – a misguided spell from the sorcerer has sent coins spilling all over the campsite. How many coins can you find?

LOOT TABLE

It can be tricky to know what to buy for the adventurer in your life. But never fear – DUNGEONS & DRAGONS are here for you, with some brilliant official products that are going to be a hit with fans of all ages.

WIZKIDS MINIATURES

For those who want to bring Tiamat, the ruler of the chromatic dragons and notable resident of the Nine Hells, into their game, Wizards of the Coast now have an official pre-painted gargantuan miniature. Standing at over fourteen inches tall, it will strike fear into the heart of even the bravest adventuring party.

BAG OF HOLDING

Every party needs a place to store their weapons, loot, and all the various bits and pieces they pick up along their adventures. Now, you can own this plush bag of holding by UltraPro and have somewhere to stash your miniatures, coins, and many, many dice.

HEROES & VILLAINS CLOTHING

Want to be both comfortable and stylish? Of course you do! So why not grab yourself some of these fabulous D&D clothes? Whether you want comfy pyjamas, soft hoodies, or warm beanies, the new line of D&D apparel is here for all your snuggly needs.

CHARACTER FOLIOS

Trying to juggle your character sheets, notes, spell cards, and other bits and pieces during a game can be stressful. Luckily, UltraPro are here to help, with these class-themed folios, where you can organise and store everything you need for your character in one handy location. Plus, they come with stickers. Who doesn't love stickers?

CROCS JIBBITZ

Speaking of comfort, you can now adorn your Crocs with official D&D Jibbitz. With fun designs, including beholders, mimics, dragons, and d20s, these are fantastic conversation starters when you're out and about.

STRIXHAVEN: A CURRICULUM OF CHAOS

Originating in the world of Magic: The Gathering, *Strixhaven: A Curriculum of Chaos* brings a whole new setting to the world of D&D. A magical university, Strixhaven offers a host of campaign opportunities – including several adventures within the source book to give you a taste of the world.

Founder Dragons

The prestigious Strixhaven University was founded by five ancient dragons. Among the first beings to learn magic in the world of Arcavios, they created the university to train people to control magic safely. Each founder dragon is associated with one of the five colleges, which are named after them.

OWLINS

Strixhaven contains a new playable race – feathery, owl-like humanoids descended from giant owls of the Feywild.

Strixhaven Spells

This school will teach your character new spells that can't be found in any previous sourcebooks. Highlights include a magical dance called *kinetic jaunt*, and *wither and bloom*, a spell that invokes the powers of life and death to damage your enemies and boost your allies.

Magic Items

A party can never have too many magic items, and Strixhaven is full of them! Whether you want a Bottle of Boundless Coffee – which does exactly what it says on the tin – or a fear-repelling cuddly toy, Strixhaven has it all.

STRIXHAVEN COLLEGES

Prismari
Students in Prismari study the arts – an ideal place for mages who enjoy flashy, ostentatious, element-based forms of magic.

Lorehold
The College of Archaeomancy, Lorehold specialises in the exploration of ancient things through magic – basically fantasy archaeologists and historians.

Quandrix
The logical Quandrix is the home of Numeromancy, also known as mathematical magic. The students here will shape their magic through the study of fractals, patterns and symmetries.

Silverquill
SIlverquill is the College of Eloquence, a place where mages learn how to magically shape their words, from flowing prose to heart-stirring battle poetry.

Witherbloom
The mages of Witherbloom study the balance between the powers of life and death. Their magic involves natural components, and can be used to harm or heal.

MORDENKAINEN

When it comes to wizards, few are as widely known as Mordenkainen. Originally one of the first player characters of D&D creator Gary Gygax himself, Mordenkainen has been around since the very beginning, and his legend permeates nearly every corner of the multiverse.

FACT FILE

NAME: Mordenkainen

AKA: Lord Mage of Greyhawk, Mad Mage of Mount Baratok

FROM: Oerth, Greyhawk

CREATURE TYPE: Human

CLASS: Wizard

ABILITIES: A skilled spellcaster, who has created many spells of his own.

FIND HIM IN: *Curse of Strahd, Baldur's Gate: Descent into Avernus, Mordenkainen's Tome of Foes, Mordenkainen Presents: Monsters of the Multiverse.*

BACKGROUND

Hailing from the world of Oerth in D&D's earliest setting, Greyhawk, Mordenkainen is known for his position of neutrality, supporting neither good nor evil. Over the years, he has travelled around the multiverse, including the Forgotten Realms and Barovia, becoming embroiled in some of the most iconic moments in magical history.

MORDENKAINEN'S SPELLS

The powerful and innovative wizard brought many spells to the Forgotten Realms, including *Mordenkainen's defense against nonmagical reptiles and amphibians, Mordenkainen's faithful hound, Mordenkainen's protection from slime*, and *Mordenkainen's involuntary wizardry.*

MORDENKAINEN'S TOME OF FOES

Tap into Mordenkainen's wealth of multiverse knowledge with *Mordenkainen's Tome of Foes,* a source book containing stat blocks for dozens of monsters and other creatures from the planes of existence.

THE CIRCLE OF EIGHT

The group of powerful wizards known as the Circle of Eight, founded by Mordenkainen himself, created many innovative spells together. After the rest of the Circle were killed at the hands of the lich Vecna, Mordenkainen dedicated several years to recovering enough of his friends' remains to clone them.

BAROVIA

Following the death of the Circle of Eight, Mordenkainen travelled to Barovia in an attempt to kill the vampiric Dark Lord Strahd. Unfortunately, his plan failed, and he ended up trapped in the demiplane for many years, being gradually driven mad by Strahd's machinations.

VIRTUAL PLAY WEEKENDS

Games of D&D are no longer limited to game shops and home games. With the growth of online play, Wizards of the Coast have started offering virtual play weekends to allow RPG lovers from all around the world to meet each other and get their roleplay on.

WHAT'S A VIRTUAL PLAY WEEKEND?

Virtual play weekends function as mini-conventions that DMs, players, and game designers can attend to meet friends, play one-shots, and discover the newest Adventurers League quests. You can join games for two or four hours, and there are even Learn to Play adventures for D&D newbies. This is very similar to the games hosted at in-person gaming conventions, but with the added bonus that you can play from the comfort of your own home, wherever you are in the world.

WHAT SHOULD I EXPECT?

After signing up for a game of your choice, you can join a group of friends or soon-to-be-friends, along with an imaginative DM, to play through an adventure – entirely online. The games on offer are a mix of brand-new Adventurers League games, non-Adventurers League games designed by the DMs, and games using older editions (even going back to the classic first edition rules, if that strikes your fancy).

FOR DMS

If you're a Dungeon Master and fancy running your own game at a virtual play weekend, you can! There are plenty of opportunities to sign up and host your own online table at any of these exciting events.

NEW CONTENT

Much like in-person conventions, one of the best things about virtual play weekends is the ability to access brand new content before the rest of the roleplaying world gets to see it. Be the first to discover the newest campaigns, seasonal content, and information on other upcoming events.

SOUNDS GREAT! HOW DO I GET INVOLVED?

The virtual play weekends are hosted by D&D partner Baldman Games, and are run once a month. Hop over to **yawningportal.dnd. wizards.com** to find out when the next game is happening, and sign up to join a table!

BESTIARY

ABERRATIONS AND UNDEAD

Some of the most iconic nasties in the D&D world fall into the category of either aberration or undead. Whether you're venturing through the Underdark or travelling the Sword Coast, even the bravest adventurers need to be on the lookout for these foul fiends.

INTELLECT DEVOURER

CHALLENGE RATING: 7

Imagine a walking brain with a bad temper. Intellect devourers are low-level servants of the better-known mind flayers, consuming the thoughts and memories of their enemies. They then take over the minds of their victims, driving their bodies around like puppets.

WHAT CAN THEY DO?

Just as their name suggests, they can devour your Intellect! Not only can they inflict some hefty psychic damage, they can also reduce your Intelligence score to 0 on a particularly effective attack.

WHERE DO YOU FIND THEM?

The Underdark.

BATTLE PLAN

They're resistant to bludgeoning, piercing and slashing damage, but you can damage them very effectively using magic, fire, and poison.

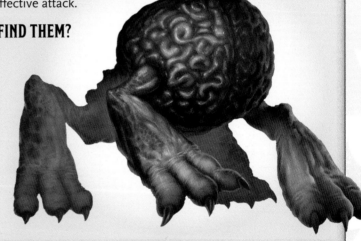

ABOLETH

CHALLENGE RATING: 10

These fishy monsters have altogether too many teeth, but that's not all that's scary about them. Hailing from the plane of madness, the Far Realm, they have terrifying psionic abilities that target the minds of those who cross them.

WHAT CAN THEY DO?

Besides spreading deadly disease with their creepy mucus and poisoned tentacles, aboleths have the ability to dominate the minds of their enemies, communicating with them telepathically, and controlling their actions.

WHERE DO YOU FIND THEM?

The Far Realm, or dark, wet, underground parts of the Material Plane.

BATTLE PLAN

Luckily, despite their ability to do large amounts of damage, aboleths don't have any resistances or immunities, so any old attack will hurt them. It's a good idea to put your highest Wisdom characters front and centre, to avoid the aboleth convincing one member of your party to turn on the others.

GHOUL
CHALLENGE RATING: 1

Ghouls lie somewhere between ghosts and zombies. The main difference is, while zombies like to devour brains, ghouls feast on flesh. They lurk in the darkness, ambushing travellers. However many victims they consume, they are cursed to never be full.

WHAT CAN THEY DO?

They don't have much in the way of combat abilities – just attacking with teeth and claws – but their bites can paralyse you if you're unlucky.

WHERE DO YOU FIND THEM?

Anywhere in the Forgotten Realms.

BATTLE PLAN

Their paralysing attacks don't affect elves, so if you have any elves in your party, get them up in the melee. They're immune to poison, charm, and exhaustion, but perfectly susceptible to a good old-fashioned axe wound.

DEATH TYRANT
CHALLENGE RATING: 15

Combining aberrations and undead, a death tyrant is basically an undead beholder – an iconic monster that represents a ray-firing floating eye. Often commanded by powerful wizards, they have necromantic powers that allow them to summon undead servants.

WHAT CAN THEY DO?

Much like beholders, they have several eye rays which give off different magical effects, including a charm ray, a disintegration ray and a death ray.

WHERE DO YOU FIND THEM?

In their lairs, which are often in the Underdark.

BATTLE PLAN

Go into any death tyrant battle prepared, because they can't be charmed, exhausted, paralysed, or poisoned. They're still susceptible to most magical and normal attacks, but be ready to take a lot of damage yourselves in the process.

DEATH IN THE FORGOTTEN REALMS

Though it isn't necessarily fun, death and dying aren't quite as permanent in the Forgotten Realms as they might be elsewhere. With clerics wielding spells like *revivify*, and a number of mages summoning undead servants, death isn't always the end in D&D.

ONE-SHOTS

One-shots are self-contained campaigns that last a single session, and are a staple of every good DM's repertoire. Here are some tips for setting up your own one-shot.

WHY PLAY ONE-SHOTS?

One-shots are great little games that can be slotted in anywhere. Maybe half of your usual party can't make it to a session, but the others want to play. You might have a group of people who want to play but can't commit to a longer session. Your players might want to test out new characters, or the DM may want to playtest a new setting. They're also a great way to lure in new players who've never played before.

HAVE A CLEAR ENDGAME

Give your one-shot a clear endgame, whether that's tracking down a MacGuffin, winning a contest, completing a dungeon, or defeating a baddie. With less time to wander around, players will need a clear goal to aim for.

SIMPLE CHARACTERS

As one-shots are quite short, it's best to keep your PCs simple (unless, of course, you're planning to reuse them in a longer campaign). Rather than having a detailed backstory that can play out over multiple sessions, stick to a few basic staples for your personality, fears, and motivations.

SPLIT IT INTO SCENES

As a general rule, a one-shot should be split up into three to five "scenes", including the final confrontation, puzzle, or encounter.

Scene Template

Scene 1: Roleplay encounter
Scene 2: Combat encounter
Scene 3: Puzzle encounter / skill challenges
Scene 4: Final combat encounter

VARY ENCOUNTERS

The type of encounters you include in your game will depend on your own play style, and what your players like to do, but it's good to keep a one-shot varied. Mix up one or two combat encounters with opportunities for roleplay, skill challenges, and general exploring. As always, it's important to strike a good balance!

LET CHAOS REIGN

One of the best things about running a one-shot is that you can let things go off the rails and not have to worry about that affecting the rest of the campaign. Follow the classic rule of improvisation: say "yes, and" to everything. When your player wants to do something chaotic, let them, and then add your own rules and ideas on top of that. Then see where it goes!

◆ OFFICIAL ONE-SHOTS ◆

There are several official sourcebooks that contain one-shots and short adventures. Try the Unwelcome Spirits campaign in *Explorer's Guide to Wildemount* for lower level characters, or dig into *Tales from the Yawning Portal* and *Ghosts of Saltmarsh*.

WHICH D&D CLASS ARE YOU?

Not sure which character to play in your next campaign? Struggling to pick between bards and barbarians? This quiz is the solution to all of your problems.

1 **You've found yourself in trouble with a local gang. How do you deal with it?**
a. I talk my way out of it.
b. With a generous sprinkling of violence.
c. There's a spell for that.
d. By beating a hasty retreat.
e. By turning into a bear.

2 **Where can you be found at a party?**
a. Being the centre of attention.
b. Tearing up the dancefloor. Literally tearing it up.
c. Firing off some impressive illusion spells.
d. Skirting the edges and pinching drinks.
e. Turning into a bear to avoid social interaction.

3 **When you're not adventuring, how do you spend your free time?**

a. Performing on every stage in the Forgotten Realms.
b. Staying in shape – it never hurts to be prepared.
c. Studying the arcane arts.
d. Some light, relaxing crime.
e. Exploring the forest. As a bear.

4 **A tavern brawl breaks out. Where are you?**

a. Somewhere near the back, shouting encouragement or heckling, depending on my mood.
b. I probably started it, if we're being honest.
c. Hiding behind something sturdy, letting off pot shots.
d. Attacking from the shadows.
e. I'm that big bear in the middle of it all.

5 What's your chosen weapon?

a. My natural charm.
b. The biggest sword, axe or club I can find.
c. My impressive arsenal of spells.
d. Daggers, a classic.
e. My sharp teeth and claws, gained by turning into a bear.

6 What's your greatest fear?

a. Being ignored or forgotten.
b. Sudoku.
c. Losing control.
d. Being the centre of attention.
e. Bear traps.

7 You find a bag of gold on the ground. What do you do?

a. Ask around town until I find the owner.
b. Leave it. I have little interest in money.
c. A simple *locate person* spell will find the owner.
d. Take it. Finders keepers, it's my gold now.
e. Turn into a bear and sniff out the owner.

ANSWERS

Mostly As
Bard. You love being centre of attention and can use your natural charm to get out of almost any situation.

Mostly Bs
Barbarian, monk or **fighter.** You're a tank at heart. You're never more comfortable than when you have a weapon in hand and an enemy to defeat.

Mostly Cs
Wizard, sorcerer or **warlock.** What's the point of not doing magic when you could be doing magic?

Mostly Ds
Monk or **rogue.** You operate from the shadows, striking before your enemy even knows you're there.

Mostly Es
Druid. If there's a problem that can't be solved by a little shapeshifting, you haven't found it yet.

GIRLS GUTS GLORY

If you love actual play, hilarious women, and complete and utter chaos, then do we have the show for you! *Girls Guts Glory* is an all-female group who dress up, play Dungeons & Dragons and film it, so we can join in the fun.

ORIGIN STORY

Girls Guts Glory started with sisters Kimberly Daugherty and Erika Fermina, who shared a love of fantasy. "Erika and I used to create stories as kids with our stuffed animals," DM and player Kim tells us. "D&D taps into that part of our imagination. I'm a screenwriter and so I volunteered to DM, not really knowing what I was getting myself into, but we got a group of girlfriends together and jumped right in!" Since that first game, they've livestreamed dozens of games, which you can catch on the official D&D Twitch and YouTube.

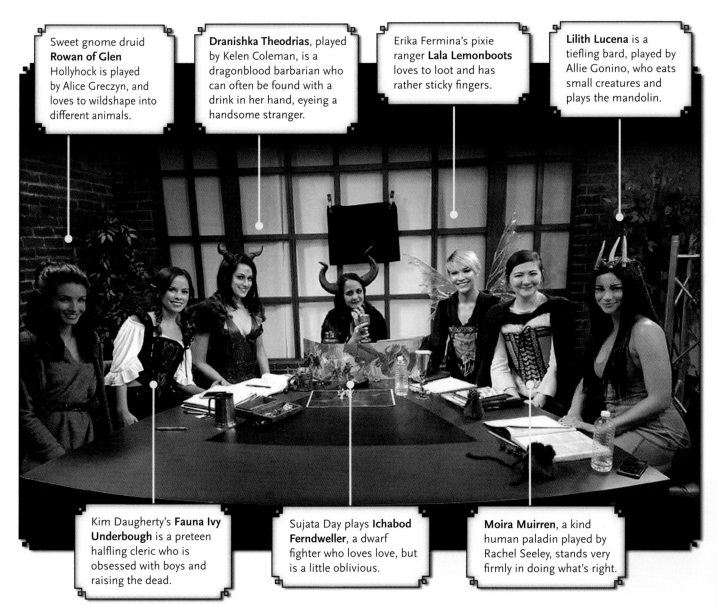

Sweet gnome druid **Rowan of Glen Hollyhock** is played by Alice Greczyn, and loves to wildshape into different animals.

Dranishka Theodrias, played by Kelen Coleman, is a dragonblood barbarian who can often be found with a drink in her hand, eyeing a handsome stranger.

Erika Fermina's pixie ranger **Lala Lemonboots** loves to loot and has rather sticky fingers.

Lilith Lucena is a tiefling bard, played by Allie Gonino, who eats small creatures and plays the mandolin.

Kim Daugherty's **Fauna Ivy Underbough** is a preteen halfling cleric who is obsessed with boys and raising the dead.

Sujata Day plays **Ichabod Ferndweller**, a dwarf fighter who loves love, but is a little oblivious.

Moira Muirren, a kind human paladin played by Rachel Seeley, stands very firmly in doing what's right.

THE FEYWILD

Girls Guts Glory have played in lots of different settings, but this DM has one sure favourite. "You know me, I always love the Feywild! Anything fairy, unicorn, magic! When my schedule was getting busier and we were looking for a new DM, we played a game with Kelly Lynne D'Angelo. She set the game at a unicorn festival and we were immediately sold!" They were so sold, that they asked Kelly Lynne to stay on as their new DM, giving Kim the chance to take on a player character within the game.

FINDING YOUR PEOPLE

These days, the women of *Girls Guts Glory* are all extremely active members of the brilliant D&D community, but Kim admits that they were a little apprehensive at first. "Being all females and newer players on the scene, we were worried about how the community would react to us streaming our games," she said. Unsurprisingly, they soon found that there was nothing to worry about! "We were greeted with open arms and have had nothing but love and support from the community! We're so grateful to be part of such a loving and inclusive community."

GETTING CREATIVE

"I'm a big fan of homebrewing," Kim tells us of her worldbuilding approach. "My number one rule for D&D is to have fun and, as a DM, I really wanted my players to let their imaginations run wild. My sister wanted to be a pixie, so we homebrewed that for her! D&D does such a great job of creating a world and guidelines to play in that also allows for interpretation and creativity."

KIM'S ADVICE

For Kim, the game is simply about having fun. "Don't be intimidated! Just jump right in. Having fun with your friends should be the number one priority. The manuals are wonderful guides but there's a lot of room to get creative too."

LEVEL UP YOUR TABLE

Nothing elevates a gaming table quite as easily as a battle map. Including a map makes it easier to visualise encounters, helps players to engage, and makes everything run much more smoothly.

BATTLE MAP BASICS

The basis for every battle map is a grid of squares. Each square represents five feet, making it really clear how far apart everything is, and how far a character can move per turn. From there, you can start adding walls, buildings, furniture, traps, and anything else you want.

ONLINE BATTLE MAPS

Playing online? There are plenty of resources available to create online battle maps, whether that's making your own on Roll20 or using one of the many fan-made maps available for use. Sites like Roll20 allow everyone to interact with the map as they play.

── HOW DOES COVER WORK? ──

Half cover: Adds +2 to AC and any Dexterity saving throws
Three-quarters cover: Adds +5 to AC and Dexterity saving throws
Total cover: Cannot be directly targeted by attacks (including spells)

MINIATURES AND TOKENS

If you've got a physical map, you can customise it using miniatures and tokens. For longer-running campaigns, players may want to have a particular miniature for their own character. You can also get generic ones for different NPCs and enemies.

PLAYING WITH ENVIRONMENT

Using movable tokens allows the DM to customise the map as you play. They can be used to add difficult terrain, throw in surprise features, and monitor spell effects, fire, and other changeable elements.

MAPPING THE REALMS

GREYHAWK

Before the Forgotten Realms, there was Greyhawk. One of the earliest campaign settings, this world of high fantasy was originally the setting of some of the D&D founders' home games, and has been embedded in D&D lore since the very beginning.

WHERE IS GREYHAWK

Greyhawk can be found on the world of Oerth, and is dominated by four continents, the most prominent of which is Oerik. A classic high fantasy corner of the multiverse, Greyhawk is home to several different groups of humans, alongside elves, dwarves, halflings and, gnomes. Another immense underground dungeon – the Undermountain – is explored in 5e's *Waterdeep: Dungeon of the Mad Mage*.

THE FREE CITY OF GREYHAWK

Located in Flanaess, the most documented part of Oerik, the Free City of Greyhawk gives the whole area its name. It's a powerful city-state that has retained its position by steering clear of most wars that have plagued the area. alongside elves, dwarves, halflings and, gnomes.

THE AZURE SEA

While this turbulent sea is bordered by many important trading posts, and frequented by merchants, it is also plagued with fierce pirates and vicious sea monsters, up to and including dinosaurs.

GHOSTS OF SALTMARSH

If you're a fifth edition player and want to explore the world of Greyhawk, the *Ghosts of Saltmarsh* anthology contains a selection of short classic adventures in and around the coastal village of Saltmarsh on the Azure Sea. Featuring undead sailors, mysterious pirates, dark cults, and, importantly, mechanics for epic sea battles, this is ideal for parties up to level 12.

THE PANTHEON OF GREYHAWK

Greyhawk is a highly religious place, with over a hundred different deities worshipped by its inhabitants. Most of these gods are human, though there are also elf, dwarf, halfling, gnomish, and orc gods, alongside a whole variety of monstrous gods and smaller cults. This makes Greyhawk an ideal campaign setting if you're interested in some clever cleric mechanics.

THE GREYHAWK WARS

Much of Greyhawk's history and politics have been shaped by the continent-wide Greyhawk Wars, initiated by destructive and chaotic demigod, Iuz. These wars, involving numerous cities, clans, and factions, raged for two years, before finally ending in the Pact of Greyhawk, a tenuous peace treaty.

CASTLE GREYHAWK

Just north of the Free City is Castle Greyhawk, built by the Mad Archmage Zagig Yragerne. Sitting atop an immense dungeon, rumoured to have fifty layers, disturbing stories of a dark curse upon this now-ruined castle have kept most adventurers at bay.

A GUIDE TO ANIMAL COMPANIONS

Whether you're a beastmaster, a wizard who needs a familiar, or just an animal lover, there are more and more options to have an animal pal in-game.

FINDING YOUR COMPANION

There are a few different ways to befriend a critter in D&D. It may come as part of a class feature, as the result of a spell, or just from a particularly successful animal handling check.

BEASTMASTER RANGERS

A classic animal lover, these rangers gain a companion at level three, when they choose their ranger conclave. There are two options: a straightforward animal companion, or a primal beast with slightly more capabilities than your everyday animal.

FIND FAMILIAR

For wizards, this spell allows you to summon a celestial, fey, or fiend that takes the form of whatever animal you choose. These creatures have the added bonus of a telepathic connection with their wizard, who gains the ability to see through their familiar's eyes, when needed.

HOMUNCULUS SERVANTS

Why summon or befriend an animal when you can build your own? Artificers have the ability to create a homunculus servant, a magically-animated mechanical creature that acts much like a familiar.

CREATE YOUR OWN

The *Player's Handbook* and *Monster Manual* contain stats for potential animal companions – popular choices include bears, mastiffs, and panthers – but you can always homebrew your own, too.

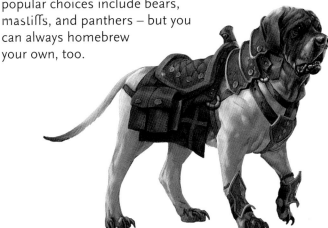

COMPANION CAPABILITIES

Your companion's combat capabilities will vary from creature to creature, but usually they act on their own turn in initiative, and can attack, dash, dodge, or hide. Most of the time, they will act on your command, though they don't need an order to take a reaction.

Usually, the player will control the animal companion on combat, but when it comes to day-to-day roleplay, the player and DM will have to decide between them who controls the companion. Both options can be fun, so have a conversation about your plans and decide which will work best for your pal.

ABILITIES

Pick two to three abilities for your companion. These can be taken from existing beast stat blocks, or entirely homebrewed. Think about combat capabilities and any specific skills you want them to specialise in.

NATURAL WEAPONS

It's unlikely that your animal companion would have a weapon, so instead focus on their natural weapons: teeth, claws, maybe horns. They should be classed as melee weapons, and between 1d4 and 1d8 piercing or slashing damage is standard.

STATS

A good rule for basic beast stats is:
HP: 1d10 per level
DC: 10 + Dexterity modifier

○	0	Strength
○	+3	Dexterity
○	0	Constitution
○	+2	Intelligence
○	+2	Wisdom
○	+7	Charisma
		SAVING THROWS

SESSION ZERO

Starting a new D&D game is a big commitment, both for DMs and for players. Enter Session Zero. This is a pre-campaign session where the whole group can sit down together and make a plan for the campaign, both in terms of story and real life.

PLANNING YOUR CHARACTERS

First and foremost, this is a chance to plan your characters. It's likely that most people will have an idea of who they want to play already, but Session Zero allows everyone to work out how their PC fits in with the setting, what their goals are, if there are any pre-existing relationships between characters, and how they all came to be in the same place.

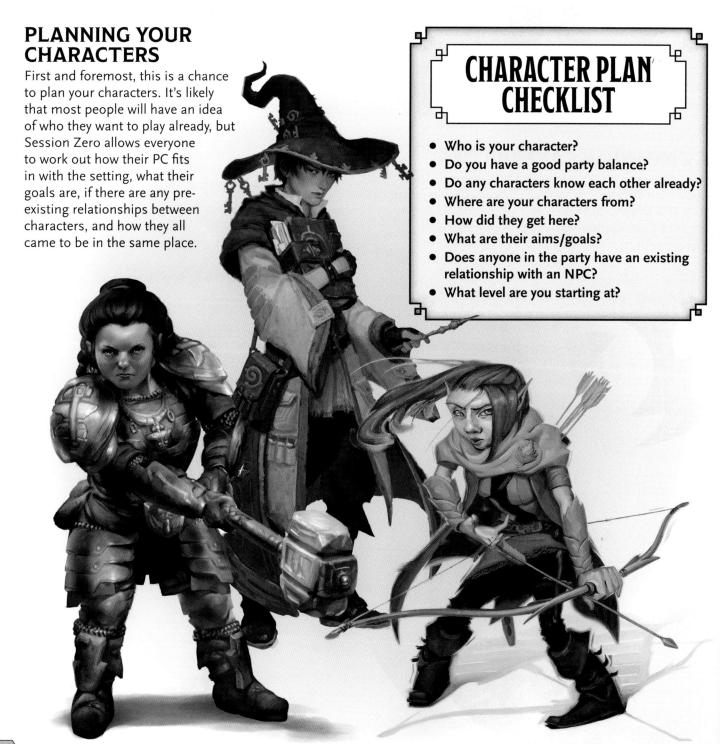

CHARACTER PLAN CHECKLIST

- Who is your character?
- Do you have a good party balance?
- Do any characters know each other already?
- Where are your characters from?
- How did they get here?
- What are their aims/goals?
- Does anyone in the party have an existing relationship with an NPC?
- What level are you starting at?

SAFETY TOOLS

Importantly, in Session Zero, you can discuss any undesired topics, any phobias or triggers that you may want to avoid, and what to do if somebody feels uncomfortable during the game. Some tables use X cards, a card that players can use if they want to avoid a particular scenario or subject without feeling the need to explain why.

CREATING THE WORLD

While the DM will likely want to keep the bulk of the campaign under wraps, they can give players an overview of the setting itself. This may be a group experience, where players can contribute their own ideas – whether that's factions, locations, or political manoeuvring – or the world may be entirely created by the DM. Both are great options, and Session Zero is a good time to decide how collaborative the worldbuilding will be.

TABLE ETIQUETTE

You can also use Session Zero to talk about your expectations for the table and the game. Will there be snacks? Will the game be more combat- or RP-heavy? How serious or silly is the tone? Is character death a high risk or not? Will there be one big quest or lots of smaller ones? It's important that everyone's on the same page from the beginning.

HOUSE RULES

Finally, draw up your house rules. Are there any things you'll be adding or removing from the standard rules? Will you be tracking gold or encumbrance? How does Inspiration work? Are there any homebrew mechanics that anybody wants to introduce? Players will come to the game with different experiences, and it's always fun to include new and interesting ideas.

FAMILY RESEMBLANCE

The Tealeaf brothers are a notorious group of rogues who cause endless havoc in Waterdeep – but they're nearly impossible to tell apart. Using the clues below, can you work out which one was responsible for starting a brawl in the Yawning Portal?

THE CULPRIT DOESN'T HAVE AN IDENTICAL TWIN • THE CULPRIT HAS HIS EAR PIERCED
THE CULPRIT HATES WEARING BEIGE • THE CULPRIT HAS NO SCARS

Ⓐ WANTED
For Misdemeanours

Ⓑ WANTED
For Chicken Theft

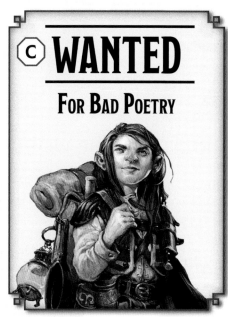

Ⓒ WANTED
For Bad Poetry

Ⓓ WANTED
For Not Bathing

Ⓔ WANTED
For Enciting a Dance-Off

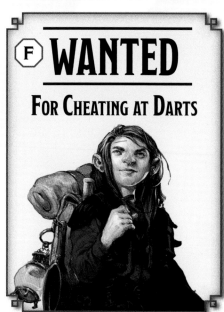

Ⓕ WANTED
For Cheating at Darts

SPEED RUN

The rogue has successfully retrieved the loot hidden at the centre of a vampire's lair – but they've woken the vampire up in the process! Help them find their way out of the dungeon as quickly as possible.

↓ EXIT

ANSWERS ON PAGES 92-93

VOLOTHAMP GEDDARM

If you need to know anything about anything, then Volo's your man. A travelling scholar and wizard, he is driven by curiosity – often to the point of landing himself in some very sticky situations.

BACKGROUND

Little is known of Volo's life before he began his travels, but he makes up for that by popping up all over the place. Gathering useful information and scandalous gossip, Volo isn't one to hoard his knowledge, either, he has written numerous books based on his adventures all around the Forgotten Realms.

VOLO'S GUIDES

Volo's first book, *Volo's Guide to All Things Magical*, caused some arcana drama as a group of powerful mages, who didn't want their magical secrets becoming public knowledge, tracked down and destroyed all copies. Since then, he's written numerous other guides, including *Volo's Guide to Monsters* and *Volo's Guide to Waterdeep*.

MARCO VOLO

Real name Marcus Wands, this bard and thief is an ongoing irritation to Volo, using his name to cover up his petty crimes and gain prestige.

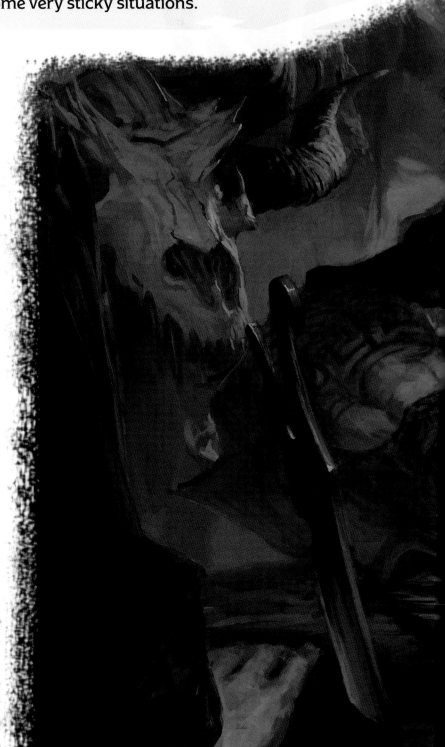

VOLO'S GUIDE TO MONSTERS

You, too, can be the proud owner of one of Volo's renowned guides, with *Volo's Guide to Monsters*. Containing dozens of new monsters and beasts, this is a must-have for every DM who loves a bit of tricky combat.

BAROVIA

At some point in his travels, Volo joined the host of legendary explorers who travelled to the vampire-controlled demiplane of Barovia, after being hired to do so by a rival. It did not go well for Volo, and he narrowly escaped a nasty fate by using a charm given to him by an old friend.

FACT FILE

NAME: Volothamp Geddarm

AKA: Volo

FROM: The Forgotten Realms

CREATURE TYPE: Human

CLASS: Wizard

ABILITIES: Not much of a fighter, Volo's strength is in his in-depth knowledge of the Forgotten Realms and its goings-on.

FIND HIM IN: *Tomb of Annihilation, Waterdeep: Dungeon of the Mad Mage, Waterdeep: Dragon Heist, Volo's Guide to Monsters.*

KNOW THE LINGO

When you're new to the wonderful world of D&D, you'll notice all sorts of strange terms being thrown around that you won't find in the rulebooks. Luckily, we're here to provide a definitive guide to D&D slang.

A GUIDE TO D&D SLANG

Above the Table
A conversation between players (or players and the DM) that happens outside of the game itself.

BBEG
Big Bad Evil Guy (or Big Bad Evil Girl) – the main boss or enemy in a campaign.

Crit
Critical – either a critical hit (natural 20), or a critical miss (natural 1). These rolls tend to have extra effects, whether that's really good or really bad.

DMPC
Dungeon Master Player Character. This is an NPC played by the DM who joins the party for a period of time.

Homebrew
Any world, character, item, or mechanic that was created outside the official D&D rules.

Meatshield
A character, often a barbarian, with low AC but a lot of hit points, who can absorb large amounts of damage.

Metagaming
When a player uses their own knowledge beyond what their character would know (for example, knowing out-of-game that a particular monster is vulnerable to fire damage and only using fire spells, even though there's no way that their character would know this). This is often considered a cardinal sin of roleplaying.

Min-Maxing
Creating a character that's extremely high-skilled in one area, but average or below average at everything else.

Nat
Short for natural, this is the number as shown on the dice with no modifiers.

Nerf
Adjusting the mechanics of a character to weaken it.

Railroading
When the DM pushes the party in a particular direction.

RAW and RAI
Rules as Written – sticking to the official rules to the letter, as opposed to Rules as Intended, where you tweak the rules to suit the game.

Rule of Cool
Bending or adjusting the rules to allow players to do something awesome.

Rules Lawyer
A player who's incredibly picky about the rules, usually adhering to RAW.

Skill Monkey
A character without many combat capabilities, but has lots of non-combat skills.

TPK
Total Party Kill – when an entire party dies in a single session.

ELEMENTALS AND FEY

Fey and elementals are often mysterious creatures, with close ties to the natural world. As a general rule, these strange beings don't come from the Prime Material Plane – elementals hail from the elemental planes of earth, fire, water, and air, while fey come from the aptly-named and magically-charged Feywild.

MEPHITS
CHALLENGE RATING: 1/2

These tiny, imp-like creatures aren't much of a threat individually, but in large groups they can do quite a bit of damage. Their appearance and abilities depend on what elemental plane they stem from – they come in many forms, including ice, mud, fire, and dust.

WHAT CAN THEY DO?

Many mephits have an elemental breath weapon – for example, magma mephits can breathe blobs of molten lava, while ice mephits have freezing cold breath.

WHERE DO YOU FIND THEM?

They spend most of their time on the Elemental Planes, but can be found lurking around their element of choice on the Prime Material Plane.

BATTLE PLAN

Unless you're extremely low level, mephits aren't a huge threat, but that doesn't mean you want to be caught unawares by one. They are often vulnerable to a different element than their own. You'll need to be careful, though, as when a mephit dies, it will explode rather messily!

FIRE ELEMENTALS
CHALLENGE RATING: 5

As you might expect, these are beings made entirely from fire. They're notoriously persistent, and don't need food, water, sleep, or even air to survive. You may also come across equally powerful water, earth, and air elementals.

WHAT CAN THEY DO?

Fire elementals can do a massive amount of damage just by touching you with their flaming hot bodies.

Just being near one of these toasty beasts can result in a drop in hit points.

WHERE DO YOU FIND THEM?

The Elemental Plane of Fire, mostly, though some can make their way to the Material Plane, especially if summoned by a mage.

BATTLE PLAN

Don't waste your time with fire or poison attacks – these elementals are immune. Instead, magical weapons and spells that inflict acid and cold damage will be effective. Fire elementals struggle to move through water, too.

DRYADS
CHALLENGE RATING: 1

These elusive fey-maidens serve as guardians of nature and, in particular, trees. Taking the form of beautiful women with leafy features, they are largely peaceful – unless you threaten their flora.

WHAT CAN THEY DO?

Dryads are spellcasters, with the ability to cast certain nature-based spells, though they don't have many combat abilities. They can also communicate with plants and animals.

WHERE DO YOU FIND THEM?

Every dryad is magically bound to a tree, and will rarely stray far from it. If you want to find one, make your way to the nearest forest ... and try to be polite.

BATTLE PLAN

It's uncommon that you would find yourself in combat with a dryad, as they try to avoid confrontation – and humanoids in general. Even if you do end up fighting against a dryad, they're more likely to charm you than try to attack.

PLANE HOPPING

Many of these creatures are rarely found on the Prime Material Plane, where most adventures take place. If you want to expand your repertoire of creatures, a *plane shift* spell can send you hurtling onto a completely different plane, filled with a whole new host of monsters.

QUICKLINGS
CHALLENGE RATING: 1

They may be small, but quicklings are fast ... and extremely devious. Though their machinations rarely amount to more than pranks, they aren't fans of humanoids and can be vicious when the situation calls for it.

WHAT CAN THEY DO?

Coming from the Feywild, they often display some magical abilities, though most of the time they prefer to attack with sharp knives and daggers. Quicklings are ambush fighters, so keep your eyes peeled!

WHERE DO YOU FIND THEM?

They can mostly be found in the Feywild and Feydark, but you wouldn't be surprised to bump into a group of them in forests around the Forgotten Realms.

BATTLE PLAN

Quicklings are more likely to lay a trap or play a trick than attack you, but if they do attack, then simple weapons and spells should do the trick. Though they're tiny, be careful, as their magic can be surprisingly destructive.

MEET THE DM: B. DAVE WALTERS

Of all the Dungeon Masters in the world of D&D, there aren't many as busy (or as talented) as B. Dave Walters. Appearing in everything from Dimension 20 to Critical Role, as well as being a writer, DM and creator, there are few people who know as much about the game as B. Dave.

THE BLACK DICE SOCIETY

If you'd like a taste of B. Dave Walters' iconic DM style, there's no better place to look than official stream The Black Dice Society, set in the sinister Ravenloft setting. B. Dave tells us a little about the live stream: "The Domains of Dread call out to six souls as they struggle to survive their journeys through the Mists. But behind it all, Darklords plot and scheme their own escape... even if it means our heroes' doom."

EXPLORING THE WORLD OF D&D

Having played Dungeons & Dragons for over thirty years, since a friend introduced him at the age of thirteen, B. Dave Walters is a big fan of the rich world that D&D has to offer. "I prefer to stick to canon, since I believe the main appeal of TTRPGs is getting to live your own adventures in a familiar world," he tells us. Still, he loves the flexibility and creativity of the game. "That being said, every campaign is homebrewed to a certain extent, since the way my Asmodeus, Xanathar, or Laeral Silverhand are going to come across massively different than someone else's. The exact same Curse of Strahd campaign will never play out the same way twice."

FINDING A COMMUNITY

"To me, fandom is all about a sense of belonging," B. Dave says, talking about the brilliant RPG community he's found himself in. "D&D gives us all a chance to be the heroes – or villains – we've dreamed about, and a common vocabulary to share those experiences with others."

ADVICE FROM A PRO

As one of the best professional DMs in the game, B. Dave Walters was more than happy to give some advice for aspiring Dungeon Masters. "Don't try to compare yourself to me, [Critical Role's Matt] Mercer, Aabria [Iyengar], or anyone else. You might be thinking, 'I can't do what they do,' and the truth is ... you can't. You really can't tell a story the way we do. But we can't do what you do. Only you can tell your story and take the players on your grand adventure." He believes that any game of D&D is about more than just the DM. "Remember it's a collaborative art, and everyone at the table is working together to have a good time and make some memories. Above all else, if you're thinking about trying to DM: DO IT."

MEET THE SOCIETY

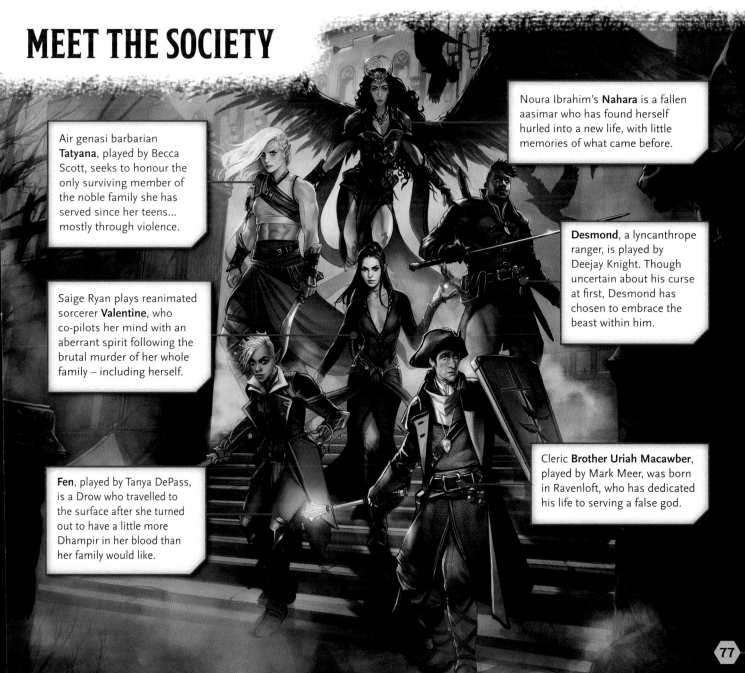

Air genasi barbarian **Tatyana**, played by Becca Scott, seeks to honour the only surviving member of the noble family she has served since her teens... mostly through violence.

Saige Ryan plays reanimated sorcerer **Valentine**, who co-pilots her mind with an aberrant spirit following the brutal murder of her whole family – including herself.

Fen, played by Tanya DePass, is a Drow who travelled to the surface after she turned out to have a little more Dhampir in her blood than her family would like.

Noura Ibrahim's **Nahara** is a fallen aasimar who has found herself hurled into a new life, with little memories of what came before.

Desmond, a lyncanthrope ranger, is played by Deejay Knight. Though uncertain about his curse at first, Desmond has chosen to embrace the beast within him.

Cleric **Brother Uriah Macawber**, played by Mark Meer, was born in Ravenloft, who has dedicated his life to serving a false god.

MAPPING IT OUT

A mysterious stranger in a tavern has given you a map that they claim leads to a dragon's hoard. Unfortunately, the map got ripped up during a fight with some goblins. Can you piece it back together?

SKILL CHECK

Picking where to put your skill scores is an important choice, as they can help define how you act as you play D&D. Can you find your next character's skills in this wordsearch?

```
R H K O F V N M T H D P K J M N B Y R S V G H P Z B W
F E P D L E N K O C V B G F N D N M K U R Y Y E B S Y
R T D G B M E D I C I N E K N I I O B R H T W R P F P
A K U Y M V K N N M O Y U F T G N C E V C F U F D L E
R E H W Z S P E P A E T M U B U V R [ I M M N O O I R
C T B Y U N O M M J E I D G N N E G P V U R K R Q N S
A B A M P E R C E P T I O N M U S Y R A L V A M L T U
N C H X A Z J S K I I N X F B S T E A L T H M A W I A
A N F O D I U B H D N A D W S Q I F S B N B S N K M S
D H B U I C N P Y L R I A F P R G W Q N S M E C F I I
Q X J E S E U S X A N I M A L H A N D L I N G E G D O
E U X Y N T U L E M O N K N H H T B R E K E I D J A N
O F C D S M T E I I U S Y C N D I F G R H E V S A T T
H E Y E J E B I G Q F I D E R I O U I Y P M L N K I I
T O H C G F Y G T U V G F R G E N V H G O D I F U O N
H G H E A J I H M X C H W R N E D Z L S M W Y K L N Z
F I D P K O V T P H T T L F R R E D B M J O O O S D H
W D U T U E Y O B U V D M Y K N R K E L U M Q N E V S
O P F I A K Y F T X R E L I G I O N E S Z O S I S B P
N S N O M O N H F J D G R E E W G X U J H I G K S O H
A A M N U U Y A B E G E D Z R U T E B R I G O Z F Z P
T G A P R N R N T M A F S S O Y D J O A S T V W C M S
U W S E O C U D O G B O E P V Y H V J B T T W R U E D
R X W P B O N U M B D D G S F E S A C R O B A T I C S
E I R N E R U V N I H N Y V G R M I L T R R U E B E V
E C S O A T H L E T I C S Y S F E R S N Y M S I K H J
M H P S Y R I T R F B U L H U B S C A D E E O G R N N
```

ACROBATICS   ANIMAL HANDLING   ARCANA   ATHLETICS   DECEPTION   HISTORY   INSIGHT   INTIMIDATION   INVESTIGATION   MEDICINE   NATURE   PERCEPTION   PERFORMANCE   PERSUASION   RELIGION   SLEIGHT OF HAND   STEALTH   SURVIVAL

LEVEL UP YOUR TABLE

Many parties are getting back to playing in-person following lockdowns – and some are even playing in-person for the first time! – here are some tips and tricks for using props to add a little pizzazz to your gaming table.

SECRET MESSAGES

Bring yourself all the way back to your school days and start passing notes! This is a great way for the DM to give messages to individual characters and for players to talk secretly with each other – perhaps using the Message cantrip. DMs can also put together mysterious notes from NPCs to give to players.

HOW TO MAKE PARCHMENT

For a more authentic feel, it's mega easy to make your own parchment-style paper.

1. Write your message on normal paper (ideally without any lines).
2. Use a paintbrush to paint tea or coffee on the paper, giving it a dark, uneven colour.
3. Put it on a flat surface and leave to dry for 1-2 hours.
4. As an additional extra, you could tear around the edges of the paper to get a nice textured feel.

POTIONS

Why not introduce real-life Potions of Healing and Heroism, using interesting-looking bottles and the colourful drink of your choice? They can be as delicious or disgusting as you like, depending how nice the DM feels.

LEGEND
The Three Odd Gables 1
University of Dementlieu 2
Phlegethan Hospital 3
Dyreth Mill 4
Red Widow Theater 5
Port-a-Lucine Opera House 6
Griool Park 7
D'Honaire Estate 8
The Crucible Building 9
Mother of Tears Cathedral 10
The Great Library 11
Palace of Enlightenment 12
Lord Governor's Manor 13
Zurich Hospital 14
Bonniville Museum of the Sea 15
Guignol's Garden 16
Delacourte Shipping 17
Palace of Ethers Park 18
Mousel Building 19
House of Wax 20

500 feet

PERNAULT BAY

GROACH ISLAND

LUCINE BAY

SEA OF SIGHS

DEMENTLIEU

BLANDO

PHYSICAL PUZZLES

Everybody loves a good riddle, but there's something about an actual physical puzzle that can't be beaten. Puzzle boxes with hidden messages inside are always a hit with players. Or you could include real-life games in your session – if a player needs to win at a game of chess or darts, bring out a chessboard or dartboard to add a whole new challenge.

DECK OF MANY THINGS

The infamous Deck of Many Things has derailed many campaigns in its time – and made almost all of them even better! Whether you have a proper Deck of Many Things, or just a modified pack of playing cards, drawing a real card, and seeing the result in front of you adds an element of tension and drama that will have your players losing their minds.

DON'T FORGET THE SNACKS!

Of course, the most important part of any in-person game is the snacks! Providing snacks that match the theme of the campaign is always fun – and delicious. If you really want to go for realism, you can serve your drinks in tankards, too.

MAPS

Not just battle maps, but proper, old-fashioned treasure maps too. Giving players a map of a particular area, perhaps with hidden or unmarked features, helps them plan their quests and is great for immersing them in the story. You can even add hidden messages to the map using lemon juice (which can be revealed by applying heat).

WILD MAGIC

There's no faster way to introduce a healthy dose of chaos into your game than using wild magic. A truly unhinged form of arcana, wild magic means that every time a spell is cast, it risks backfiring, misfiring, or causing completely random effects.

WILD MAGIC SORCERERS

Perhaps the most common source of wild magic in D&D is the wild magic sorcerer. These mages, who draw their magic from the chaos that underlies everything, must roll a d20 whenever they cast a spell. On a 1, a wild magic surge occurs – which could be great, but could also be very, very bad.

BARBARIAN PATH OF WILD MAGIC

It is not a surprise that the other class prone to a wild magic surge is the rage-driven barbarian. Powered by intense feelings of emotion, barbarians who walk the path of wild magic risk a wild magic surge every time they go into a rage. This may allow them to do extra damage on an attack, or it may cause flowers to sprout up around them.

ROLEPLAYING A WILD MAGIC SURGE

Besides being a very cool mechanic – and extremely funny or frustrating at times – wild magic offers so many opportunities for clever roleplaying. Consider how your character got their wild magic – was it inherited from their ancestors, or did it come from a particular incident? How do they feel about it? And how does their wild magic present? It could be a beautiful, innate sense of power, or a messy, chaotic explosion.

GET CREATIVE

Beyond player characters with wild magic, there are lots of ways that a DM can incorporate wild magic into a game. Potions or magic items could have the potential to cause a random magic effect. If you're creating a dungeon, why not have traps that produce wild magic effects when triggered, rather than causing damage?

CREATE YOUR OWN WILD MAGIC TABLE

Both wild magic sorcerers and path of wild magic barbarians have official wild magic tables, showing the possible effects of a surge. If you want to create your own, it's easy! Simply draw up a table with the right number of slots (for sorcerers, it's a d100 table, for barbarians it's d8) and let your imagination run wild. Random spell effects are always a good choice, plus you can throw in some truly weird effects for optimum chaos.

AVERNUS

Avernus is the first layer of the Nine Hells, a war-torn plane inhabited by devils and their kin. As the first line of defence against attacks from devils' natural enemy, demons, Avernus is a barren hellscape under constant threat of invasion.

WHERE IS AVERNUS?

The Nine Hells exist entirely on their own separate plane, connected to the Prime Material Plane via the Astral Plane. If you're brave (or foolish) enough to travel there, Avernus is the first and biggest layer you will reach.

ZARIEL

Avernus is a strictly hierarchal society, and at the top of that hierarchy is the archdevil, Zariel. Once an angel, Zariel's zealous love for war led her to fall from grace. Now, she leads the troops of Avernus against the demons of the Abyss.

CREATURES OF AVERNUS

BONE DEVILS

These sinister creatures often act as a kind of hellish police force, upholding the laws of Avernus. They relish the suffering of others, even going so far as to torment other devils.

PIT FIENDS

By far the most fearsome devils in the Nine Hells, pit fiends were once regular devils who were cleansed of any empathy or goodness in the Pit of Flame. Now they are powerful overlords of Hell.

NARZUGON

The warped souls of paladins who made a deal with a devil, narzugons are now the elite knights of the Nine Hells' armies. Riding upon hellish horses, or nightmares, a legion of these devils is a fearsome sight.

BALDUR'S GATE: DESCENT INTO AVERNUS

Explore the world of Avernus in *Descent into Avernus*. Containing encounters with powerful devils, mechanics for making pacts with devils, and stat blocks for infernal war machines, this campaign is a common favourite among DMs and players alike.

THE BLOOD WAR

Across the River Styx from the lawful evil Nine Hells is the chaotic evil Abyss, home to demons, the natural enemies of devils. For centuries, a war between these two factions raged, spanning entire planes of reality, with Avernus acting as the Nine Hells' first line of defence.

Avernus

ROLL FOR INTELLIGENCE

Fancy yourself an expert on all things *Dungeons & Dragons*? Does your monster knowledge run from aboleth to zombie? Have you read every book in Candlekeep? Take this quiz to see how your Intelligence check turns out.

1 **In which campaign setting can you find Warforged?**
a. The Forgotten Realms
b. Eberron
c. Strixhaven
d. Greyhawk

2 **What is the name of the near-immortal monster hunter who has made an enemy of Strahd von Zarovich?**
a. Rudolph van Richten
b. Jander Sunstar
c. Gary von Murder
d. Drizzt do'Urden

3 **Characters with a hexblood lineage get their power from which creature?**
a. Vampire
b. Demigod
c. Lich
d. Hag

4 **What is the first series of books to contain the hero Drizzt Do'Urden?**
a. The Icewind Dale trilogy
b. The Sundering
c. Ravenloft
d. The Dragonlance Saga

5 **What creature type is a pegasus?**
a. Fiend
b. Giant
c. Celestial
d. Elemental

6 **How many trickster gods did Acererak kill to build his Tomb of Annihilation?**
a. Seven
b. Eight
c. Nine
d. Ten

7 **Prismeer in the Feywild was split into three parts. What are they called?**
a. Here, There and Everywhere
b. Past, Present and Future
c. Thou, Thy and Moreover
d. Hither, Thither and Yon

8 **Which of these is not a type of dragon?**
a. Elemental
b. Chromatic
c. Metallic
d. Gem

9 **Which type of creature founded Strixhaven University?**
a. Angel
b. Devil
c. Human
d. Dragon

10 **Which setting does Mordenkainen hail from?**
a. The Forgotten Realms
b. Eberron
c. Strixhaven
d. Greyhawk

11 **Where do aboleths come from?**
a. The Underdark
b. The Far Realm
c. The ocean
d. The Feywild

12 **What world is Greyhawk on?**
a. Faerûn
b. Flanaess
c. Oerth
d. The Shadowfell

13 **Which class might have a homunculus servant?**
a. Artificer
b. Wizard
c. Ranger
d. Warlock

14 **Which pesky bard sometimes claims the identity of Volo?**
a. Han Volo
b. Marco Volo
c. Steve Volo
d. Volo the Second

15 **Which types of damage are fire elementals immune to?**
a. Fire and cold
b. Necrotic and acid
c. Bludgeoning, piercing and slashing
d. Poison and fire

16 **Which two classes can gain wild magic features?**
a. Sorcerer and barbarian
b. Sorcerer and wizard
c. Sorcerer and warlock
d. Sorcerer and druid

17 **Devils are native to the Nine Hells. Where are demons native to?**
a. The Ten Hells
b. The Abyss
c. The Void
d. The Far Realm

FAREWELL

And that's it! From campaign settings to actual campaigns, magic creatures to wild magic, and actual plays to home games, this Annual is just a tiny taster of all that the world of *Dungeons & Dragons* has to offer.

Now it's up to you! If you loved discovering magic creatures, then grab the *Monster Manual* or *Mordenkainen Presents: Monsters of the Multiverse* and get reading. If you've been inspired to homebrew your own game, this is the time to start! Perhaps you've found a novel you want to read, or a podcast to listen to, or a setting you really want to try. Whatever's sparked your interest, it's time to grab your bag of holding and dive headfirst into your next big adventure.

To keep up-to-date on the latest D&D news and entertainment, keep an eye on our official website, and follow us on social media.

DND.WIZARDS.COM

FACEBOOK.COM/DUNGEONSANDDRAGONS

TWITTER.COM/WIZARDS_DND

YOUTUBE.COM/USER/DNDWIZARDS

TWITCH.TV/DND

INSTAGRAM.COM/DNDWIZARDS/

GLOSSARY

A

aberration – a strange, alien-like creature, often hailing from the Far Realm.

ability – numerical characteristics that are used to determine success of actions. D&D has six core abilities: Charisma, Constitution, Dexterity, Intelligence, Strength, and Wisdom.

Abyss, the – one of the Outer Planes, home to demons.

actual play – a D&D game that is available to watch or listen to via livestream or podcast.

Adventurer's League – an ongoing official organised play campaign.

Armour Class (*also* **AC**) – a defensive stat based on a character's class and the armour they wear. Enemies must roll higher than this stat to complete an attack.

artificer – a class of magical engineers.

B

barbarian – class of adept warriors that can channel rage to increase their strength.

bard – a musical class that use poems and songs to boost abilities and cast spells.

beholder – a monster often found in the Underdark, which takes the form of a giant floating eyeball with many smaller eyes on stalks.

C

campaign – a pre-written adventure that has the basic storyline, puzzles, monsters, and more for a party to journey through and explore.

celestial – angel-like beings from the Outer Planes.

challenge rating – a numerical indicator of the difficulty of an encounter or monster.

D

d20 – a dice with 20 numbered sides. There is also a d4, d6, d8, d10, d12, and d100.

druid – a class attuned with nature and imbued with power from the natural world of deities.

Dungeon Master (*also* **DM**) – the person who leads the narrative of a campaign, sets up encounters, tasks players with puzzles, and voices all the NPCs.

E

elemental – a creature from the Elemental Planes, often representing a single element, such as fire or water.

Elemental Planes – sometimes known as the Inner Planes, these planes represent different elements.

F

Far Realm – an extradimensional plane of madness.

feat – an optional ability or area of expertise.

fey – a creature from the Feywild.

fiend – a creature from the Lower Planes.

fifth edition (*also* **5e**) – the latest version of D&D.

fighter – a character class that specialises in the use of several weapons.

first edition – the original version of D&D.

Forgotten Realms – the most prominent setting in D&D, which focuses on high fantasy.

G

Gygax, Gary – co-creator of D&D.

H

hit points – indicator of a character's health. These are depleted as a character receives attacks.

homebrew – creating your own rules, settings, items, and mechanics.

I

immunity – when a creature is impervious to a particular type of damage.

initiative – the order in which combatants take their turn, determined by a dice roll at the start of battle.

inspiration – a gift from the DM to reward good roleplaying, can be used to aid rolls.

L

lich – an undead creature, often a wizard or sorcerer who sacrificed their soul in exchange for immortality and power.

Lower Planes – realms populated by devils and demons, often associated with evil.

M

monk – a class that is a master of martial arts and can channel magic through their ki.

Multiverse – a culmination of the many different official D&D settings.

N

Nine Hells – one of the outer planes, home to devils and demons.

NPC – a non-player character, voiced by the DM.

O

Outer Planes – a selection of different planes, often organised according to alignment.

P

paladin – a class of holy soldiers, often highly armoured and able to use powerful weapons and magic.

party – the group of player characters that journey through a campaign together.

patron – an otherworldly deity or being that provides power and protection to warlocks, and occasionally whole parties.

Prime Material Plane – the primary plane where most campaigns will take place.

proficiency – a bonus modifier that is determined by your race or class.

R

ranger – a class of hunters that are adept at taking down monsters in the wild, often with a bow.

resistant – when a creature only takes half damage from a particular type of damage.

rogue – a class of dexterous, sneaky characters that often gravitate towards thievery and subterfuge.

roleplay – the act of assuming the role of a character and making decisions through another's lens.

S

saving throw – a dice roll made in opposition to an attack or action, or to avoid death when unconscious.

sorcerer – an often unpredictable magical class that can use powerful spells.

subclass – a specialisation of a base class that has a more refined focus and extra skills.

U

undead – a creature that exists between life and death.

Underdark, the – an underground region of the Forgotten Realms.

Upper Planes – good-aligned Outer Planes.

V

vulnerable – when a creature takes double damage from a particular type of damage.

W

warlock – a class that gains their magical ability through pacts with mysterious beings.

wizard – a studious magic-wielding class with a wide range of spells and knowledge.

ANSWERS

PAGE 14
Combat Chaos

The Wizard and Fighter's accounts are identical

PAGE 15
What Have You Hoard?

PAGE 30
Tomb Raiders

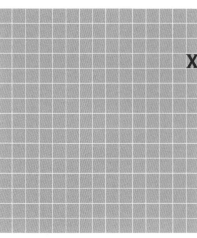

Page 31
It's Not What You Sphinx

The answer is G

PAGE 42
Spelling it Out

Lightning Bolt

PAGE 43
Cashing In: there are 24 coins

PAGE 68
Family Resemblance

The answer is E

PAGE 69
Speed Run

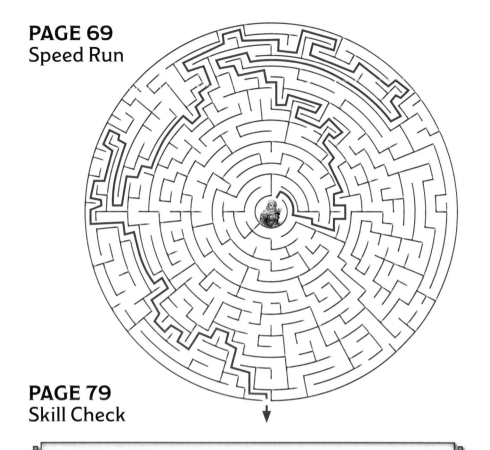

PAGE 78
Mapping it Out

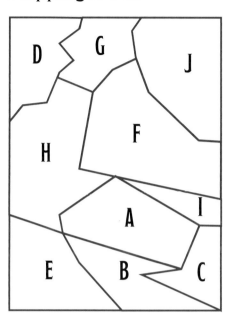

PAGE 79
Skill Check

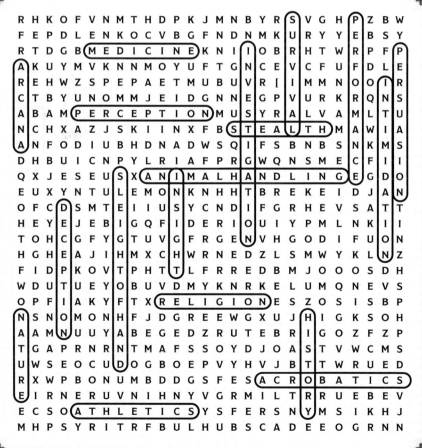

PAGE 86-87
Roll for Intelligence

1. **b.** Eberron
2. **a.** Rudolph van Richten
3. **d.** Hag
4. **a.** The Icewind Dale trilogy
5. **c.** Celestial
6. **c.** Nine
7. **d.** Hither, Thither and Yon
8. **a.** Elemental
9. **d.** Dragon
10. **d.** Greyhawk
11. **b.** The Far Realm
12. **c.** Oerth
13. **a.** Artificer
14. **b.** Marco Volo
15. **d.** Poison and fire
16. **a.** Sorcerer and barbarian
17. **b.** The Abyss